JOSEPH GRINNELL'S
Philosophy of Nature

JOSEPH GRINNELL
1877–1939

Joseph Grinnell's
PHILOSOPHY OF NATURE

*Selected Writings of
a Western Naturalist*

Essay Index Reprint Series

BOOKS FOR LIBRARIES PRESS, INC.
FREEPORT, NEW YORK

First Published 1943
Reprinted 1968 By Arrangement With
The University of California Press

LIBRARY OF CONGRESS CATALOG CARD NUMBER:

68-20304

PRINTED IN THE UNITED STATES OF AMERICA

This Volume, Among Others Thus Specially Designated, Is
Published in Commemoration of the
SEVENTY-FIFTH ANNIVERSARY
of the Founding of the University of California

Preface

IN THE BUSY life of Joseph Grinnell, time for deliberative thought often appeared to be at a premium. A man who accomplished the things he did might easily have become so absorbed in his daily tasks that the formulation of a philosophy of nature would never have taken place. But there was nothing drab or routine about Grinnell's thoughts; they were of unlimited horizon. His escape from the danger of becoming a scientific and administrative automaton resulted partly from an innate effervescence of ideas together with a sense of obligation to record them. Reading through his voluminous writings, we pick up many gems of interpretation, crystallized rapidly, often in the field, and under the stimulus of the rich perception gained from his own keen senses. He was quick to react, and the significance of events was rapidly evaluated in his mind.

A more unified fabric of thought on the subject of natural history grew from the considered statements which Grinnell prepared for introductory sections of his general works. Through the years some of these were revised frequently and were enriched by new experience. This body of thought forms the line of emphasis in the selected writings contained in this book. The selections may most benefit those persons who had no opportunity to learn directly from the teaching of this master naturalist, but they will also provide refreshment of viewpoint to the numerous company of his students.

A promise was made by Joseph Grinnell, as much to himself as to others, that upon retirement he would write a book of general scope which would present his outlook on the aspects of natural history most related to his own research. This was to be his "one book," as he put it. Happily, we have a late record in his own handwriting of an outline for this book. The memorandum, written one day in the field, gives the chapter headings. These of course would in time have been subjected to the careful scrutiny that characterized all his work. To me the topics that he jotted down envision a definite and solid structure of theory and example into which as a framework I can see him working many of the separate items contained in the collection now before us. The outline is instructive in itself and is presented here verbatim.

GEOGRAPHY AND EVOLUTION
CHAPTER
1. The concept of distributional limitation; chronological versus spatial conditions.
2. The nature of barriers; examples of different sorts of barriers in mammals and birds.
3. Distributional areas defined: realms, life-zones, faunal areas, associations; the ecologic niche.
4. Bird migration as a phase of geographic distribution.
5. Kinds of isolation; degrees of isolation as influencing results; the significance of geographic variation.
6. "Plasticity" versus "conservatism" in different groups of birds and mammals.
7. The pocket gophers and the song sparrows of California.
8. Reconcilability of geographic concept with that of genetics; species and subspecies in nature defined.
9. "Orthogenesis" from the standpoint of geographic variation.
10. The bearing of the geography and evolution upon human problems.

Through these chapter headings, and through the pages to follow, run certain themes which I may attempt to indicate. Animal life is locked in a continual struggle for existence. Everything that an organism is and does counts in the equation of survival, and its activities can and must be observed and analyzed in their finest detail. Adherence to this dictum made Grinnell staunchly neo-Darwinian in theoretical outlook. He stood for patient, scrupulous recording of facts seen in nature— for the development of honesty and thoroughness in observational technique and interpretation at a period when the vogue of experimentation was in its most rapid ascendancy. There was in his mind a sound conviction that without acute and exhaustive observation of nature the foundation of evolutionary study was lacking.

The factors which limit the distribution of animals, based on details of their reactions to environment, form a prevailing theme. Such factors are especially well set forth in his own style in the paper entitled "Presence and Absence of Animals." The metes and bounds of animal geography he surveyed with a view to their causes, histories, and correlations. Geographic limitation, and thus isolation, are the foundations of evolution, and in the geographic race which originates under these influences he clearly saw the nascent species—the most critical stage in evolution. He was, as he put it, "intensely interested in the barely discernible subspecies, because it is in the critical formative stage and there is a good chance that . . . something of the causes and essential conditions of its differentiation" may be learned.

The power of the environment to shape the characters of races of animals was a sharp reality to him. Among the striking physiographic contrasts found in the state of California, his own particular field laboratory, he was able to point out factors, climatic and biotic, which had modified many groups of vertebrate species. He showed that there are numerous differentiation centers and faunal areas which are potent regions for environmentally guided evolution. In each of these, parallel modifications are taking place in associated but unrelated species. Selection acting to develop protective resemblance was the principle most generally favored by him in explaining parallelisms in coloration.

Apart from the subject of evolution, we find papers which portray the exacting curator and the stimulating field companion. In still others we sense the philosophy of one who found pleasure in watching the behavior of linnets on a lawn and who reflected with misgivings on human standards of attractiveness when the activities of tree surgeons drove birds from the great oak outside the corner window of his office.

It is in some measure presumptuous to select from a man's writings* what one thinks are his best thoughts. From the items that we offer here each reader may properly choose his own set

---

* For a complete bibliography see *The Condor*, XLII (1940), 19–34.

of especially valued ideas. In presenting this collection, it has been my conviction and that of my colleagues, Seth B. Benson, E. Raymond Hall, and Jean M. Linsdale, that no attempt should be made to arrange the papers in any fashion other than chronologically. A chronology takes no liberty with an author's work and does permit easy tracing of the development of viewpoints. In Grinnell's own tradition, we present the original papers verbatim.

Had Joseph Grinnell lived to gather into his book on geography and evolution the fruits of his years of study in field and museum, its preface would have contained some such acknowledgment as appeared in 1937 on the first page of his preface to *Fur-bearing Mammals of California*. There he paid grateful tribute to Miss Annie M. Alexander, founder of the Museum of Vertebrate Zoölogy, whose financial support and buoyant encouragement made possible the accumulating of facts which formed the background for theories set forth in his writings. A like tribute, though unvoiced, is here.

ALDEN H. MILLER

Berkeley, California,
October 15, 1941

Contents

[xi]

Illustrations

Call Notes of the Bush-Tit

DURING three-fourths of the year the California bush-tits forage about in flocks. These bands may consist of as many as thirty individuals, but generally there are from fifteen to twenty. Although we call them flocks, they are not such in the sense that blackbirds or linnets form flocks; for the bush-tits never bunch together and mount high in air to take a prolonged flight. But they form a loitering company, scattered among several scrub-oaks or brush-clumps. There may be a general onward movement, for if a person locates himself in the midst of the restless drove, in a few minutes they will have almost all gone off in some particular direction. A few stragglers sometimes forget themselves, and suddenly feeling lost, fly helter-skelter after the main company with excited calls. Evidently there are some, perhaps two or three adults, who take the initiative, and involuntarily direct the movements of the younger or more timid individuals which follow along after. During such slowly moving excursions, each individual is rapidly gleaning through the foliage, assuming all possible attitudes in its search for tiny insects among leaves and twigs. The attention of each is on himself as a usual thing, but each is continually uttering a faint but characteristic simple location-note, a note of all's-well which indicates safety and also the whereabouts of the main body to stragglers, and each individual to any other.

At times, especially towards evening, the flocks become more restless and move along from bush to bush and tree to tree much more rapidly than when feeding, the birds straggling hurriedly after each other in irregular succession. During these hurried cross-country excursions, the simple location-notes are pronounced louder and are interlarded at frequent intervals with a shrill quavering note. The faster the band travels, the louder and more oft-repeated becomes these all-important location-notes; for the greater becomes the danger of individuals becoming separated from the main flock. Bush-tits are usually hidden from each other in dense foliage. They have no directive color-marks; therefore, being gregarious birds, the great value of their location-notes becomes apparent.

Should a bush-tit lag so far behind as to be beyond hearing of his fellows, he may suddenly come to a realization of his loneliness; he at once becomes greatly perturbed, flitting to the tallest available perch, and uttering the last mentioned note reinforced into a regular cry for his companions. This is usually heard by the distant band and several similar answering cries inform the laggard of the direction the flock has taken. Off he goes in zigzag precipitation and joins his fellows with evident relief. We may judge from the strongly gregarious habit of the bush-tits that each individual gains from the community life. Such mites of birds surely have enemies, and a clue as to the identity of one enemy, at least, was brought to my attention last summer at Pacific Grove. There I took from the nest a young sharp-shinned hawk, the stomach of which contained an adult bush-tit, in pieces of course. Those of us who have closely observed the bush-tits to any extent will certainly recall the following experience at one time or another. I myself have witnessed it scores of times. A flock of bush-tits will be foraging as usual, with the ordinary uncertain medley of location-notes, when suddenly one or two birds utter several of the sharp alarm notes and then begin a shrill quavering piping. This is taken up by the whole flock, until there is a continuous monotonous chorus. At the same time every member of the scattered company strikes a stationary attitude in just the position it was when the alarm was first sounded, and this attitude is maintained until the danger is past. In nearly every case the danger is in the shape of a hawk, more especially of the smaller species such as the sharp-shinned or sparrow hawks. No matter how close the hawk approaches, the shrill chorus continues and even intensifies until the enemy has passed. The remarkable thing about this united cry, is that it is absolutely impossible to locate any single one of the birds by it. The chorus forms an indefinably confusing, all-pervading sound, which I know from personal experience to be most elusive. It may be compared in this respect to the sound of the cicada. This confusion-chorus, as I think it might be appropriately called, is a sure sign of the appearance of a small hawk even a long way off. Often long before I could myself locate the hawk, a neighboring band of bush-tits would have set up their cry, thus announcing its approach. It seems reasonable to infer that this monotonous chorus of uncertain direction, at the same time as it sounds a general alarm, serves to conceal the individual birds, all of which at the same time maintain a statuesque, motionless attitude. Their colors also harmonize closely with the shadows of the foliage. The whole evidently forms a composite protective device, which must be, as a rule, effectual. Scarcely any attention is ever paid by the bush-tits to large hawks, such as buteos, or to other large birds such as turkey vultures, pigeons, or jays. The bush-tits seem to be able to easily identify their real enemies at surprisingly long range.

It is also of interest to note that mammals, large or small, are seldom stigmatized by the confusion-chorus. If a person, or dog, or similar animal appears among a flock of bush-tits, a bird here and there may utter a sharp repetition of the simple location-note very much augmented in volume. But after a moment's quiet, during which the birds intently survey the cause of the alarm, the flock goes on with its busy foraging, and usual miscellany of location-notes. Very often no attention at all is paid to a person, the birds flitting about heedlessly within a few feet of him.

During the short breeding season from March through May, when the flocks are disbanded and the birds are in pairs, the same notes are used between the mates. These express about the same meaning as during the rest of the year, but of course, often have to do with the nest and young. But there is no vestige of a distinctive spring-song, as I have seen ascribed to the bush-tit.

To summarize: I have attempted to describe more minutely the bush-tit's notes as they sound to me. Of course I realize how hard it is to describe bird-voices. And also, as I have often had opportunity to note, hardly any two persons receive the same impression of a single bird's song. No two people seem to hear exactly alike.

Each of the five notes defined beyond is perfectly distinct, and each at once signifies to me some particular and easily recognizable state of mind of the birds in question.

1. Faint one-syllabled simple notes, usually uttered in irregular succession while the birds are undisturbed, and intently gathering food or nest material. (*Tsit, tsit; tsit; tsit.*)

2. From one to five of the simple notes uttered somewhat more loudly and followed by a rather shrill quavering note of longer duration. This is uttered among members of a flock or between a pair of birds when not intently feeding, but when moving more or less rapidly with restless activity from tree to tree in some definite direction. (*Tsit, tsit, tsit, sre-e-e-e; tsit, sre-e-e-e.*)

3. The same as the last, that is, the one to five simple notes followed by a quavering trill, but pronounced with much more volume and emphasis, and, according to circumstances, more hurriedly. This is uttered by lone individuals suddenly finding themselves separated from one another or from the main flock. (*Tsit', Tsit', sre-e-e-e'.*)

4. Of the same quality as the simple one-syllabled note first described, but greatly intensified, and pronounced abruptly, several in rapid succession. This is uttered by parent birds when a nest is disturbed, and by a few certain individuals in a flock, upon the first appearance of any enemy. In the case of mammals, such as a cat, hog, or squirrel, or a person, this simple alarm-note is not followed by the confusion chorus to be next described. (*Tsit''; tsit', tsit'; tsit''.*)

5. A shrill quavering trill, of the same quality as described under No. 2 above, but without the preceding simple notes, and chanted continuously in a monotone by all members of a

flock for as long as two minutes. This peculiar chorus is uttered only during the presence of such an avian enemy as the sharp-shinned, Cooper, sparrow, or pigeon hawk, and owls, if these latter happen to be startled into a day-time flight, as occasionally happens. (*Sre-e-e-e-e, etc.*)

The Origin and Distribution of the Chestnut-backed Chickadee

THE Chestnut-backed Chickadee (*Parus rufescens*) is a boreal species of peculiarly limited distribution. It is almost exclusively confined to the humid Pacific Coast region of North America, within which it is the most abundant, and in many places the only, member of the genus *Parus* present. We find it characteristically at home within the densest coniferous forests, or along their edges, where there is much shade and an even temperature.

The range of the Chestnut-backed Chickadee is nearly two thousand miles long north and south, extending from a little north of Sitka, Alaska, to some forty miles below Monterey, California. (See Map I.)* But its width is very narrow, only within the confines of Oregon and Washington exceeding one hundred miles and elsewhere usually much less, save for one or two isolated interior colonies to be mentioned later.

The influences determining this queer-shaped distribution area may be safely assumed to be atmospheric humidity, with associated floral conditions. For this habitat coincides quite accurately with the narrow coastal belt of excessive cloudy weather and rainfall.

The specific character distinguishing *Parus rufescens* from all other American chickadees is the color of the back, which is an intense rusty brown approaching chestnut. It is of common note that the most evident effects of similar climatic conditions on other animals is a corresponding intensification of browns, especially dorsally. We may therefore consider the Chestnut-backed Chickadee, as indicated by its chief specific character, to be a product exclusively of the peculiar isohumic area to which we find it confined.

Parus rufescens, from Sitka to Monterey, has a chestnut-

* Map omitted.

[7]

colored back. And from Sitka to Point Arena, between which we find the extremest humidity, another conspicuous character is uniform,—the color of the sides, which are also deep rusty brown. But from Point Arena south to San Francisco Bay (Marin District), these lateral brown areas suddenly weaken to pale rusty; while from San Francisco south past Monterey (Santa Cruz District), adult birds have the sides pure smoke gray without a trace of rusty. (See Map II.)*

The species thus presents geographic variation within itself, and three distinguishable forms have been named, respectively, the Chestnut-sided Chickadee (*Parus rufescens rufescens*), the Marin Chickadee (*Parus rufescens neglectus*), and the Santa Cruz Chickadee (*Parus rufescens barlowi*). But all three subspecies are unmistakably the Chestnut-backed Chickadee (*Parus rufescens*). (For detailed descriptions, distribution and synonymy see beyond.)†

This southward paling of the lateral feather tracts seems to be parallel to the relative decrease in the humidity of the regions occupied. But still, even the Santa Cruz District with its gray-sided *barlowi* has very much greater rainfall and cloudiness than regions immediately to the southward and interiorly. The too abrupt aridification with accompanying sudden floral changes apparently forms the present barrier to further distribution in these directions.

The paling of the sides in the southern bird seems to be a secondary condition, as I hope to show further on by age comparisons. We can reasonably infer that *Parus rufescens rufescens* was the ancestral form from which *Parus rufescens neglectus* and then *Parus rufescens barlowi* successively arose through exodus distally from its point of differentiation further north, where the faunal conditions were doubtless then as now most effective.

First, as to the origin of the species, *Parus rufescens*. Can we find a chickadee now occupying a faunal area which can be considered as nearer the common ancestral form than *rufescens* now is?

---

* Omitted.   † Omitted.

An affirmative answer seems plausible when we come to consider *Parus hudsonicus,* which occupies the interior of Alaska and British Columbia east to Labrador and Nova Scotia. This wide-ranging boreal species also affects coniferous forests, and according to my own experience possesses life habits quite similar to those of *Parus rufescens;* in fact to me indistinguishable. The latter differs from *Parus hudsonicus* in smaller size and particularly in shortness of tail. The color areas on the two species are coextensive, but the colors themselves are different in intensity. The top of the head in *hudsonicus* is broccoli brown, while in *rufescens* it is dark hair brown. The back of *hudsonicus* is pale grayish olive brown, while in *rufescens* it is chestnut brown. The sides and flanks of *hudsonicus* are rather pale hazel brown, while in *rufescens* they are deep hazel brown approaching chestnut. Otherwise the two species look practically alike.

These differences are just those we find so commonly in two conspecific representatives, one occupying an arid habitat, the other a comparatively more humid one. Indeed we can find exactly parallel cases in certain other bird races occupying the same two regions as the chickadees in question, but which as yet are not disconnected by intermediates, and in which the degree of difference is not so great. (For example, *Melospiza lincolni lincolni* and *Melospiza lincolni striata,* and *Regulus calendula calendula* and *Regulus calendula grinnelli.*) It is the same story, of intensification of browns and decrease in size under the conditions of a moist climate.

As to the greater relative decrease in length of tail in *rufescens,* it may be suggested that it is an observed rule among the Paridæ (and in some other birds of similar habits, though not without exception) that those species which habitually forage highest above the ground in the foliage of tall trees possess the relatively shortest tails, while conversely those which haunt low thick trees or underbrush exhibit the greatest caudal development. (For example, *Psaltriparus* and *Chamæa.*) These conditions doubtless bear some definite relation to mode of flight.

The shorter the flights the slower they are, and therefore the greater must be the tail surface distally in furnishing sufficient opposition to the air to direct or arrest flight. At any rate, *rufescens* haunts much higher and more open trees than *hudsonicus*.

It seems to me reasonable to suppose that *Parus hudsonicus* approaches closely the common ancestral form. Its wide range, which, if we take the Old World *Parus cinctus* of such close resemblance as conspecific, is almost holarctic, favors this idea. At some early period there may have been no representative of *Parus* in the Northwest Coast belt. By a process of invasion of individuals of the hypothetical stock form (which we may call *Parus pre-hudsonicus*) from the adjacent region, and their subsequent gradual response to the new set of environmental factors, a geographical race became differentiated which might have then been properly called *Parus pre-hudsonicus rufescens*.

Unfortunately this process, which I believe to be constantly going on among all animals, is so slow that its actual operation under natural conditions has so far defied direct observation and measurement during a man's lifetime. But it seems quite logical to consider the natural process identical with that under 'artificial' conditions, where the rate is readily perceptible.

We seem warranted in considering all observed living forms, including 'species', and completely isolated (insular) as well as intergrading 'races' as just a momentary glimpse, so to speak, of a tree-like branchwork slowly rising through time, some of the limbs ramifying freely and rapidly, others growing slenderly without offshoots, but all advancing continually, though changing in outward appearance at different rates; only we at our brief glance can see but a horizontal section, that is, only the set of *tips* of this otherwise ancestral tree.

Accepting this standpoint as the most reasonable hypothesis yet presented, and moreover not at variance with our facts, I feel justified in judging of the methods of ramification and progress through time from observation of the existing set of 'tips' (= species and subspecies). Among these, from the nature of the case, we should be able to recognize various stages in the process of species formation, and from these judiciously selected steps demonstrate the completed stairway which leads up from the very incipiency of differentiation (as impossible of ultimate detection by us as the vanishing point) to the complete separation of two distinct species. The steps are of course really infinite in number, like the points in a geometrical line; the transition proceeds gradually without a break.

In tracing the hypothetical lines of development of the chickadees, I do not feel guilty of bold speculation; for I am only attempting to express in a selected case what is to me clearly evidenced from a survey of bird races in general.

As has already been asserted, *Parus rufescens* doubtless arose as a geographical race of *Parus pre-hudsonicus*. It is now called a 'species' because intermediates have dropped out; in other words, the divarication is now wholly complete and there are two separate twigs. The area of intermediate faunal conditions between the humid coast belt and the arid interior region of British Columbia and Alaska is very narrow, consisting, in places personally traversed by me, of but a few miles over a mountain ridge. This very narrowness of the area of faunal mergence probably accounts for the lack of intermediates at the present day between *hudsonicus* and *rufescens*.

The center of distribution of any animal is where the greatest rate of increase is. The greatest rate of reproduction is presumably where the species finds itself best adapted to its environment; and this is also where the death rate is least, unless an enemy rapidly multiplies so as to become a serious check. In a wide-ranging species, or one that is rapidly spreading over a region of varying climatic and associated conditions, subcenters of distribution will arise at points which prove to be more favorable, in point of food supply and minimum of enemies, than intervening areas. From each of these new centers of distribution there will be a yearly radiating flow of individuals into the adjacent country, so as to escape intra-competition at any one point.

Such centers of distribution will obviously, as time goes on, harbor only locally pure-bred individuals, for foreign individuals will not stem the tide of population from season to season slowly emigrating. This will amount to operative isolation and allow of the time necessary for the impress, by local factors of environment, of incipient characters, which, through cumulative inheritance as the element of time further increases, become to us perceptible and characterize this set of individuals as a geographical race or 'subspecies.'

Let us suppose that descendants from the interior *Parus prehudsonicus* from season to season pushed their way further and further into the primæval coast belt until the latter supported a vigorous colony. The coastal humidity was very likely at that time but slightly greater than that of the interior, having gradually increased through slow shifting of ocean currents or other causes, so that the faunal boundary was not so abrupt and did not then as now constitute a formidable barrier to invasion.

Faunal conditions are without doubt undergoing constant alteration. Endemic animals must adaptively respond or else be exterminated or restricted to the places where faunal change is slowest. The possibility at once presents itself of *Parus prehudsonicus* having been already native of the coast before the latter became faunally distinct from the interior. But in either case the original populating of the region must have been through invasion from elsewhere, as effected by shifting climatic conditions.

At any rate a center of distribution must have arisen in the new region of different faunal conditions. Just as quick as the new colony began to reproduce fast enough to furnish a return flow of individuals the immigration of individuals bearing the inherited stock characters from the parent region would be checked. This would mean that the new colony would become a new center of differentiation because of the isolation thus afforded. (As to what brings about the acquisition or change of innate characters, whether by natural selection or some other more direct cause, we need not here try to discuss.)

As the dissemination of individuals to prevent congestion of population will be continually away from the centers of distribution, it follows that the characters newly acquired at the centers where the rate of differentiation is greatest will be constantly carried away from those centers. If the region of intermediate faunal conditions were narrow, as in the present case, individuals bearing the inherited characters impressed by their separate areas of differentiation would from generation to generation invade toward each other until intermediates would be swamped, or there might be an unfit strip left between where neither would flourish. This might be bridged over by hybrids for a while. But the specific characters becoming strengthened by time would make hybridization less and less likely to take place, and there would result the two distinct species as we now know them.

In the case of *Parus rufescens* and *Parus hudsonicus* there seems to be now a narrow hiatus between the two. At least I can find no record of the two species having been found in the same locality. The narrowness of the region of intermediate faunal conditions may therefore be considered as the reason why we do not find connecting links between *hudsonicus* and *rufescens* at the present time. For the amount of difference between these two chickadees does not strike me as any greater than, for instance, between *Melospiza cinerea montana* and *Melospiza cinerea rufina,* between which there is continuous distribution and free interosculation. But we cannot expect any two species of birds or other animals to present the same degrees of differentiation in the same length of time or under the same conditions, much less under different conditions. For in no two animals is the physical organization in all respects exactly the same.

In a given aggregation of individuals constituting a new colony a certain amount of time is necessary for the set of environmental factors to become operative in bringing about new inheritable characters to a degree perceptible to us. Then the inherited effects of invasion and crossbreeding from season to season from the adjacent parent center of differentiation will be evidenced less and less, as time elapses, as the distance from this center increases. The offspring of successively further removed unions will, of course, inherit to a less and less degree the distinctive characters of the ancestral stock on one side and more and more of the incipient ones on the other.

If, now, the distance is great enough to permit of the time required for adaptive manifestations to become innate, then we would find new characters making their appearance distally nearest the new center of differentiation. If the distance were too short we would not find new characters showing themselves because they would be constantly crowded down by the influx of the old. The time factor may therefore be reduced by the intervention of an impassable barrier. As an instance we find three (and there are probably two other) insular forms of the Song Sparrow within a limited distance among the Santa Barbara Islands, while through the same distance on the adjacent mainland there is but one. Or in the case of continuous distribution the time element may be comparatively lessened by the great distance between the range limits, and it may be still further decreased as these limits lie in faunal areas of more emphatically different nature. The Horned Larks as well as Song Sparrows furnish us several good examples of the latter two rules.

It is *isolation,* either by barriers or by sufficient distance to more than counterbalance inheritance from the opposite type, that seems to me to be the absolutely essential condition for the differentiation of two species, at least in birds.

A strong argument in support of this conviction is that we never find two 'subspecies' breeding in the same faunal area, and no two closely similar species, except as can be plainly accounted for by the invasion of one of them from a separate center of differentiation in an adjacent faunal area. An appropriate instance in illustration of the latter is the occurrence together in the Siskiyou Mountains of northern California of the brown *Parus rufescens* of the wet coastal fauna and the gray

Parus gambeli of the arid Sierran fauna. (See Anderson & Grinnell, Proc. Ac. Nat. Sc. Phila., 1903, p. 13.) The Siskiyou Mountains occupy a line of mergence between the two faunæ, and the two respectively representative chickadees have evidently extended their ranges toward each other until now over this one small area they occupy common ground. Several parallel cases could be cited; their significance seems obvious.

We come now to consider the origin of the races of *Parus rufescens*. In a species of recent arrival into a new region (by invasion from a neighboring faunal area), as it adapts itself better and better to its new surroundings, granted the absence of closely related or sharply competing forms, its numbers will rapidly increase. This means that there will be increased competition within the species itself, on account of limited food supply. The alternative results are either starvation for less vigorous individuals during recurring seasons of unusual food scarcity, or dissemination over a larger area. In a way the first might be considered as beneficial in the long run, as doubtless leading to the elimination of the weaker; such a process evidently does take place to a greater or less degree all the time, and is important for the betterment of the race. But as a matter of observation Nature first resorts to all sorts of devices to ensure the spreading of individuals over all inhabitable regions; in other words, the extremest intra-competition does not ensue until after further dissemination is impossible. In birds we find a trait evidently developed on purpose to bring about scattering of individuals. This is the autumnal 'mad impulse' which occurs just after the complete annual moult, when both birds-of-the-year and adults are in the best physical condition, and just before the stress of winter food shortage. Even in the most sedentary of birds, in which no other trace of a migratory instinct is discernible, this fall season of unrest is plainly in evidence. I may suggest not unreasonably that autumnal migration may have had its origin in such a trait as this, the return movement in the spring becoming a necessary sequence. (See Loomis, Proc. Cal. Acad. Sc., 3rd Series, Zoölogy, II, Dec., 1900,

352). It is a matter of abundant observation that autumn is the season when we find the most unlooked-for stragglers far out of their normal range, and when sober, stay-at-home birds, like *Pipilo crissalis* and the chickadees, wander far from the native haunts where they so closely confine themselves the rest of the year. It is also the experience of collectors that the greatest number of these stragglers are birds-of-the-year, which thus, obeying the 'mad impulse', are led away from their birthplace into new country, where they may take up their permanent abode, and be less likely to compete with their parents or others of their kind. Then, too, crossbreeding of distantly related individuals is more likely. The records of the Santa Cruz Chickadee outside of its regular breeding range are all of August to October dates (Haywards, Gilroy, San Jose, etc.).

Thus, as above indicated, by the occupancy of new territory the number of individuals which can be supported will correspondingly grow. Hence a vigorous colony will spread out along lines of least resistance, being hindered by slight faunal changes, but completely checked only by topographic or abrupt climatic barriers. *Parus hudsonicus* and its near relative *Parus rufescens* are boreal species, the former inhabiting the Hudsonian Zone and the latter a certain portion of the Canadian. It seems reasonable to suppose that *rufescens* differentiated in the northern part of the humid coast belt, which has been called the Sitkan District. This is a faunal subdivision of the Canadian Zone, and its northern part approximates more closely Hudsonian conditions than southerly. Granting that the early center of differentiation and distribution of *Parus pre-hudsonicus rufescens* was in the northern part of the Sitkan District, then the route of emigration would be confined to the narrow southward extension of that faunal area. The habitat of *Parus rufescens* thus gradually acquired the long north and south linear appearance as shown at this day. But when the pioneer invaders at the south reached the vicinity of Point Arena, they met with somewhat changed temperature and consequent floral conditions, but not so abrupt as to constitute a permanent barrier. Doubtless the progress of invasion was retarded until adaptive modifications evolved, which correlatively allowed of further invasion, until the abrupt limits of the Santa Cruz District were reached.

San Francisco Bay and the Golden Gate seem to now form a pretty effectual barrier between *neglectus* on the north and *barlowi* on the south. At least, among the large number of skins examined by me with this point in view, I can find none from one side that can be confidently determined as being identical with the race on the other. Neither chickadee has been found east of the bay, nor anywhere nearly so far from the coast belt, except for one record of a specimen taken in the fall at Haywards. This has been reëxamined and proved to be *barlowi*, as was to be expected from its contiguity. However, the Golden Gate is so narrow that an occasional crossing may take place. This was more probable formerly, when the redwood timber grew up to the Gate on both sides. Heermann in 1853 recorded the species from "San Francisco." But now, I think, the bird is unknown for several miles on either side of the Gate. Doubtless this barrier accounts in part for the origin of the distinct form *barlowi* within so short a distance.

As to the distance to which a species may invade, we can surmise that, topography permitting, theoretically there is no limit so long as adaptive modifications continually take place. The geographic variation in *Melospiza* may be called to attention as an extreme illustration. But practically, in the case of *Parus rufescens barlowi,* much further invasion is improbable, because in adjoining areas are already firmly established members of the same family (*Bæolophus, Psaltriparus, Chamæa*) thoroughly adapted to prevailing food conditions. No one of these could probably be successfully competed against by a foreigner. Every animal tends to increase at a geometric ratio, and is checked only by limit of food supply. It is only by adaptations to different sorts of food, or modes of food getting, that more than one species can occupy the same locality. Two species of approximately the same food habits are not likely to remain long evenly balanced in numbers in the same region. One will crowd out the other; the one longest exposed to local conditions, and hence best fitted, though ever so slightly, will survive, to the exclusion of any less favored would-be invader. However, should some new contingency arise, placing the native species at a disadvantage, such as the introduction of new plants, then there might be a fair chance for a neighboring species to gain a foothold, even ultimately crowding out the native form. For example, several pairs of the Santa Cruz Chickadee have taken up their permanent abode in the coniferous portion of the Arboretum at Stanford University, while the Plain Titmouse prevails in the live oaks of the surrounding valley.

In accordance with the above outlined theories of distribution it is easy to account for isolated breeding colonies, such as that of *Parus rufescens rufescens* in northern Idaho (Fort Sherman and Cœur d'Alene Mountains). Fall stragglers, wandering unusually far and finding themselves suddenly amid familiar conditions, would tarry there to breed, and with the continuance of a favorable state of affairs, and with no serious competition, might soon result in a well-established colony, itself a center of distribution. The record of *rufescens* from Mt. Shasta (July 14) seems to have been based on a lone straggler, for the species has not been found there since. (For references and localities see beyond.)*

As has become a generally accepted idea, the young plumages of birds, if different at all from those of the adults, present a generalized type of coloration; or, to express it in another way, the young more nearly resemble recent ancestral conditions. The familiar examples of the spotted, thrush-like plumage of the young robin and the streaked, sparrow-like plumage of young towhees and juncos are cases in point. Accepting this phylogenetic significance of ontogeny, we find the chickadees giving some interesting illustrations.

Although the adult of *barlowi* has the sides pure smoke-gray,

---

* Omitted.

the juvenal plumage possesses pale rusty sides. This points towards a rusty sided ancestor like *neglectus*. This also agrees perfectly with the distributional evidence of origin. The adult of *neglectus* has pale rusty sides; the young also has rusty sides, but somewhat darker than in the corresponding age of *barlowi*, and moreover is more nearly like the juvenal plumage

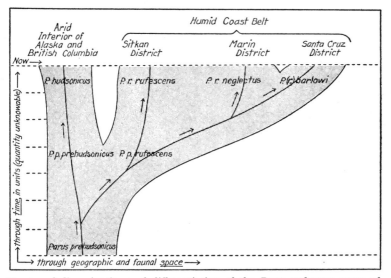

Routes of dissemination and differentiation of the *Parus rufescens* group of chickadees.

of *rufescens*. But the sides in adult *rufescens* are deep brown, almost chestnut, while the young has much paler, merely dark rusty sides. And what is most significant is that the young of *rufescens* and *hudsonicus* are much nearer alike than are the adults, the former having only very slightly darker rusty on the flanks. The young of *hudsonicus* in respect to intensity of browns almost exactly equal the adults of the same species, showing that the present coloration is of very long standing, and offering further evidence that *hudsonicus* is nearest the common stock form of all the chickadees under consideration. Juvenal characters, resembling ancestral conditions, lag behind the newer acquired adult characters.

To repeat: The young of *barlowi* has the sides paler rusty than *neglectus*, *neglectus* slightly paler than *rufescens*, but *rufescens* has the sides slightly more rusty than *hudsonicus*, a sequence which accords well with the present theories of origin. (See Map III.)*

* The accompanying illustration on page 19 has been redrawn from the graph which was entitled Map III in the original publication.

Composition of the Prince William Sound Avifauna; Discussion of Its Origin

THE ANIMAL and plant life of the Prince William Sound region clearly belongs to two life zones, the Hudsonian and Alpine-Arctic. The former is practically coincident with the timbered areas, which extend from sea-level to an altitude varying from 1,000 to 1,600 feet, and is confined to a relatively narrow tract bordering the sea shore and extending up the valleys. (See plate 34.)* The Alpine-Arctic, or treeless, zone covers the tops of the mountains on the islands, and the interior land-mass which surrounds the Sound.

The birds of the region appear to be groupable zonally as follows:

1. Land-birds believed to breed in the Hudsonian zone of the Prince William Sound district:

Canachites canadensis atratus
Accipiter velox
Archibuteo lagopus sancti-johannis
Haliaeëtus leucocephalus alascanus
Bubo virginianus lagophonus
Ceryle alcyon caurina
Dryobates pubescens glacialis
Selasphorus rufus
Empidonax trailli alnorum
Pica pica hudsonia
Cyanocitta stelleri stelleri
Corvus corax principalis
Corvus brachyrhynchos caurinus
Pinicola enucleator flammula
Loxia leucoptera
Passerculus sandwichensis alaudinus
Junco hyemalis hyemalis

Melospiza melodia kenaiensis
Melospiza lincolni gracilis
Passerella iliaca sinuosa
Hirundo erythrogaster palmeri
Tachycineta thalassina lepida
Vermivora celata lutescens
Dendroica aestiva rubiginosa
Dendroica townsendi
Wilsonia pusilla pileolata
Cinclus mexicanus unicolor
Nannus hiemalis pacificus
Certhia americana montana
Penthestes rufescens vivax
Regulus satrapa olivaceus
Regulus calendula grinnelli
Hylocichla guttata guttata
Ixoreus naevius meruloides

2. Land-birds believed to breed in the Alpine-Arctic zone of the Prince William Sound district:

Lagopus rupestris kelloggae
Leucosticte tephrocotis littoralis

Acanthis linaria linaria
Anthus rubescens

---

* Omitted.

Osgood (N. A. Fauna no. 19, 1900, p. 16, foot-note) has called attention to the fact that the humid Pacific Coast belt of Alaska is not uniform all the way from Dixon Entrance to Kadiak Island. The forested region south of Lynn Canal is largely dominated by the Canadian life zone, and to it should be restricted the term "Sitkan district." The forested coast belt from Lynn Canal and Cross Sound to the Alaska Peninsula is purely Hudsonian, but not to be considered a part of the Yukon faunal district as intimated by Osgood. It appears to be divisible into distinct faunal areas as follows: Yakutat Bay district, Prince William Sound district, Cook Inlet district, and Kadiak district. Too little work has been done in the Yakutat Bay district to warrant a discussion of its relationship further than to assert that, from what is known, it is more nearly like the Prince William Sound district than the Sitkan district. The former, as shown by the comparative lists of component species given beyond, although of the Hudsonian zone, is quite distinct from the Yukon district.

Absence of satisfactory data prevents a comparison of the avifauna of the Prince William Sound district with that of the Cook Inlet district or with that of the Yakutat Bay district. But enough is known of the Sitkan and Yukon faunas to warrant the following comparisons. It is almost superfluous for me to urge that the status here given to any species is of necessity tentative. Not until field work has been carried on throughout the year in representative localities, as by Nelson at St. Michaels, can we be certain of the seasonal and distributional status of each of the birds in the respective faunas.

The water-birds are of little service in characterizing the avifauna of Prince William Sound. With the exception of *Ardea herodias fannini* and *Branta canadensis occidentalis,* the species are either transients, or of wide distribution. The two exceptions are characteristic species of the Sitkan district, and do not occur in the interior of Alaska, nor much further to the westward along the Pacific Coast.

3. Prince William Sound birds which are believed to be merely transients from the Yukon district:

Circus hudsonius

Falco columbarius

Calcarius lapponicus alascensis

Zonotrichia coronata

Dendroica coronata hooveri

Penthestes atricapillus turneri

4. Breeding land-birds of the Prince William Sound district which occur also quite generally throughout Alaska:

Accipiter velox

Archibuteo lagopus sancti-johannis

Haliaeëtus leucocephalus alascanus

Ceryle alcyon caurina

Corvus corax principalis

Loxia leucoptera

Hirundo erythrogaster palmeri

Dendroica aestiva rubiginosa

Anthus rubescens

Cinclus mexicanus unicolor

5. Breeding land-birds occurring in the Prince William Sound and Yukon districts but not in the Sitkan district:

Bubo virginianus lagophonus

Empidonax trailli alnorum

Pica pica hudsonia

Acanthis linaria linaria

Passerculus sandwichensis alaudinus

Junco hyemalis hyemalis

Tachycineta thalassina lepida

Certhia americana montana

Ixoreus naevius meruloides

6. Breeding land-birds occurring in the Prince William Sound and Sitkan districts but not in the Yukon district:

Dryobates pubescens glacialis

Selasphorus rufus

Cyanocitta stelleri stelleri

Corvus brachyrhynchos caurinus

Pinicola enucleator flammula

Leucosticte tephrocotis littoralis

Melospiza lincolni gracilis

Vermivora celata lutescens

Dendroica townsendi

Wilsonia pusilla pileolata

Nannus hiemalis pacificus

Regulus satrapa olivaceus

Regulus calendula grinnelli

7. Breeding land-birds of the Prince William Sound district which do not occur in either the Yukon or Sitkan districts:

Canachites canadensis atratus

Lagopus rupestris kelloggae

Melospiza melodia kenaiensis

Passerella iliaca sinuosa

Penthestes rufescens vivax

Hylocichla guttata guttata

8. Some land-birds of the Sitkan district not also found in the Prince William Sound district:

Dendragapus obscurus fuliginosus

Lagopus lagopus alexandrae

Buteo borealis alascensis

Dryobates villosus harrisi

Sphyrapicus ruber ruber

Colaptes cafer saturatior

Empidonax difficilis

Loxia curvirostra sitkensis

Spinus pinus pinus

Junco hyemalis oreganus

Hylocichla ustulata ustulata

Planesticus migratorius caurinus

9. Some land-birds of the Yukon district not also found in the Prince William Sound district:

Bonasa umbellus umbelloides
Lagopus lagopus lagopus
Surnia ulula caparoch
Dryobates villosus leucomelas
Picoides americanus americanus
Euphagus carolinus
Acanthis hornemanni exilipes

Spizella monticola ochracea
Zonotrichia leucophrys gambeli
Lanius borealis invictus
Dendroica striata
Seiurus noveboracensis notabilis
Penthestes hudsonicus hudsonicus
Hylocichla aliciae

To review the faunal characteristics as indicated by the foregoing lists, the Prince William Sound district possesses thirteen breeding land-birds in common with the Sitkan district (list no. 6), and nine in common with the Yukon district (list no. 5). Besides these, there are ten species which occur throughout all three districts (list no. 4), and six which are not found in either the Yukon or Sitkan district (list no. 7). Of this last category, *Canachites canadensis atratus* is closely similar to *C. c. osgoodi* of the Yukon district; and as this bird has no analogue in the Sitkan district, it is clearly a recent derivative from the Yukon fauna. The same is evident of *Lagopus rupestris kelloggae*. On the other hand, *Penthestes rufescens vivax* is most nearly related to the *P. r. rufescens* of the Sitkan district, and has no near relative in the Yukon district. This subspecies may, therefore, be considered a contribution from the Sitkan fauna. However, as I have elsewhere suggested (Auk XXI, July, 1904, p. 368), *P. r. rufescens* was itself, though much more remotely, derived from *P. hudsonicus* of wide boreal range. *Melospiza melodia kenaiensis, Passerella iliaca sinuosa,* and *Hylocichla guttata guttata* are likewise most nearly allied to representatives in the Sitkan district; the same or near related forms extend also to the westward through the Cook Inlet region.

That there are not more endemic species of birds in the Prince William Sound region, and that the species which *are* peculiar are so slightly differentiated, appear to be due to its small area, and to the relative narrowness and ineffectiveness of the barriers which surround it. The barrier for the Hudsonian species is the arctic-zone divide which surrounds the Sound in the form of a semicircle, with only a long, narrow coastal connectant along the Kenai Peninsula to the westward, and another towards Yakutat Bay to the eastward. The only endemic arctic-zone species (*Lagopus rupestris kelloggae*) owes the opportunity for its differentiation to the isolation afforded by the mountains on the more remote islands of the Sound. (See p. 384.)*

That the Prince William Sound region has not produced as divergent forms of birds as the other faunal areas of Alaska may be due also to its more recent service as a center of differentiation. We may assume that there were no land-birds at all in the Prince William Sound region at some remote period. This is a reasonable assumption from the seesaw-like elevation and depression to which the Alaskan coast has been subject, and which is even now in operation. Then the present avifauna is composed of birds which have entered the region from elsewhere, these having been permitted to do so as the new region became inhabitable and as the intervening barriers allowed. An examination of the present ornis of the region shows that all the species represented may be traced to the two different sources already referred to, now geographically contiguous to the Prince William Sound region, namely, the Yukon and Sitkan districts. These two faunal areas had already become differentiation centers at least before the Prince William Sound region had become more than a meeting ground of invading species.

Migrants may pass regularly over a wide area; yet the evidence teaches us emphatically that migrants do not ordinarily stop in their semiannual movements and start breeding centers at any point where the conditions become attractive (as is often assumed). Birds, whether migratory or sedentary, invade a new territory only by gradual extension of their *breeding* areas from season to season, physiographic conditions permitting.

That there is apparently no geographic variation in the birds of the Sound from island to island or from island to mainland is possibly due either to (1) the narrowness of intervening

---

* Page 384 of the original publication is not included here.

waterways, so that they may be so frequently crossed as to swamp by inbreeding any developing centers of differentiation; (2) the relative uniformity of ecologic conditions throughout the region, so that the forces are lacking which would carry on rapid divergent speciation; or (3), the submergence of the region and resulting isolation of colonies, so recent as not to have allowed sufficient time for the differentiation of local forms with perceptible characters. It is entirely possible that all three of these factors have contributed to the condition of uniformity displayed throughout the region by such susceptible birds as Melospiza and Passerella.

In conclusion, it is safe to say that the Prince William Sound avifauna, although younger than the Sitkan and Yukon avifaunas, and of a lower rank, is nevertheless well marked. This contention is based on the peculiar association of species which characterizes it, and upon the inclusion in it of several forms which appear to have differentiated within the region itself.

Melanism in the Endemic Species

A survey of the three faunas here discussed, to ascertain the general characters displayed by the respectively component species, shows that, in the birds of the Sitkan and Prince William Sound districts as compared with corresponding species of the Yukon fauna, there is an increase in the extent of black markings and a darkening of the shades of brown and green, and a reduction in the general size, and disproportionate shortening of the wings and tail. (See table on page 425.)*

The melanism referred to includes the most conspicuous specific and sub-specific characters of the birds (and many other terrestrial animals) of the coastal region of southeastern Alaska notorious for its heavy rainfall. This correlation of heavy pigmentation with large precipitation, and *vice versa*, has been so generally observed and commented upon that the latter has often been advanced as a cause for the former. The correlation is an observed fact; but it is not yet acceptably explained

---

* The table is on page 28, here.

am I able to adduce any new evidence to solve the matter. A discussion of the present status of the problem may not prove out of place.

The "humid coast belt" of Alaska, as compared with the more arid interior, offers four obvious environmental conditions: (1) an extreme of precipitation—rainfall, heavy mists, fog; (2) a high relative humidity of the atmosphere when not actually saturated; (3) a very large percentage of cloudy days— that is, much shade; (4) impeded radiation and therefore a much more uniform temperature, free from the extremes of the arid region.

That the melanism in question is caused by precipitation directly (although this is often assumed) appears to be abundantly disproven by the occurrence of palely colored species in regions of great annual rainfall, as in the Sierra Nevada of California. Here the rain, averaging in places 70 inches per year, comes in brief, heavy storms interspersed with prolonged periods of clear weather. Furthermore, in the coastal region of central California, with an annual rainfall of but 25 inches, various deeply colored subspecies have differentiated. Here, however, there is a great preponderance of cloudy days. But it is clearly not a matter of actual precipitation.

Neither does the influence of a humid atmosphere appear to be a direct cause of normal melanism, the experiments of Beebe to the contrary notwithstanding. (See Zoologica: Contributions of the New York Zool. Soc. I, 1907, pp. 1–41.) For the newly hatched young and the young in newly acquired juvenal plumage show as great relative depth of coloring as the adults which have undergone many molts, and which have been for their lifetime bathed in the humid atmosphere. And furthermore, dark-colored birds, members of "humid" faunas, in instances known to me remain for several generations imperceptibly changed when artificially transplanted into a relatively more arid climate, or when they have naturally extended their range beyond the confines of the humid faunal area in which they were with little doubt originally differentiated.

TABLE LISTING CORRESPONDING BIRDS OF THREE ALASKAN FAUNAS, TO SHOW RELATIVE CONDITIONS OF SIZE AND MELANISM

Yukon District.	Prince William Sound District.	Sitkan District.
Ixoreus naevius meruloides, large, pale.	Ixoreus naevius meruloides,[1] large, pale.	Ixoreus naevius naevius, small, dark.
Regulus calendula calendula, large, pale.	Regulus calendula grinnelli, small, dark.	Regulus calendula grinnelli, small, dark.
Penthestes hudsonicus hudsonicus, large, pale.	Penthestes rufescens vivax, large, dark.	Penthestes rufescens rufescens, small, dark.
Certhia americana montana, large, pale.	Certhia americana montana, large, pale.	Certhia americana occidentalis, small, dark.
Vermivora celata celata, large, pale.	Vermivora celata lutescens,[1] small, dark.	Vermivora celata lutescens, small, dark.
Passerella iliaca iliaca, large, pale.	Passerella iliaca sinuosa, smaller, slaty.	Passerella iliaca townsendi, small, ruddy.
Melospiza lincolni lincolni, large, pale.	Melospiza lincolni gracilis,[1] small, dark.	Melospiza lincolni gracilis, small, dark.
Junco hyemalis hyemalis, large, slaty.	Junco hyemalis hyemalis, large, slaty.	Junco hyemalis oreganus, small, ruddy.
Passerculus sandwichensis alaudinus, pale.	Passerculus sandwichensis alaudinus,[1] pale.	Passerculus sandwichensis savanna, dark.
Pinicola enucleator alascensis, large, pale.	Pinicola enucleator flammula, small, dark.	Pinicola enucleator flammula, small, dark.
Hylocichla ustulata swainsoni,[1] large, slaty.		Hylocichla ustulata ustulata, small, ruddy.
	Hylocichla guttata guttata,[1] large, pale.	Hylocichla guttata nana, small, dark.
Dryobates pubescens nelsoni, large, pale.	Dryobates pubescens glacialis, small, dark.	
Dryobates villosus leucomelas, large, pale.		Dryobates villosus harrisi,[1] small, dark.
	Melospiza melodia kenaiensis,[1] large, slaty.	Melospiza melodia rufina, small, ruddy.
Canachites canadensis osgoodi, pale.	Canachites canadensis atratus, dark.	
Bubo virginianus lagophonus,[1] ruddy.	Bubo virginianus lagophonus, ruddy.	Bubo virginianus saturatus, blackish.
Planesticus migratorius migratorius, large, pale.		Planesticus migratorius caurinus, small, dark.

[1] Not typical.

As intimated in the second paragraph preceding, the correlation of dark-colored species of birds with areas of excessive cloudiness, irrespective of rainfall, is so general as to demand serious consideration. Although an apparent fact, its significance is far from clear. Exposure to intense light from a cloudless sky (as with the human species and certain other animals) induces an increased deposit of dermal pigment. But in many others, the tone of coloration of the surroundings, whether black lava or white sand, appears to be assumed, irrespective of the mean light intensity. It is held by some, and with good grounds if the matter is not pressed too far, that the tone of coloration of such birds as do not find it advantageous to be conspicuous, tends to harmonize exactly with the average or blended tone of the background, against which they "disappear" when motionless. This mean background varies in depth of tone directly with the percentage of cloudiness. This idea is upheld by the fact that the most typically dark-colored humid-belt birds are such as either regularly serve as prey or are predaceous; as the grouse, ptarmigan, fox and song sparrows, juncos, thrushes, owls and certain hawks. Crows, ravens, swallows, hummingbirds, eagles, fish hawks, and some water-birds respond indifferently in this regard. Such "protective" coloration would have been acquired through gradual increments from individual variation, by the action of natural selection. But this theory is discountenanced by many on grounds it is not here necessary to discuss. That the light itself has no direct effect on the colors of birds at the time of pigment deposition in the forming feather is shown by the fact that the characteristic depth of coloring is acquired by young birds hatched and fledged within dark holes of trees, as woodpeckers and chickadees.

In well-known regions there is often much difference in climate from year to year, one year showing a much greater or lesser amount of cloudy weather than the next. There is nothing to show that relevant species of birds in the same region become darker during cloudy years. The characters are constant from year to year. The melanism is an inherited character, not modified during the life of the individual, except because of age by means of molt, and by such adventitious agencies as abrasion and bleaching.

The effect of temperature on color in birds is not indicated by any evidence that I know of. The conspicuous difference in temperature affecting sedentary birds in the Yukon and Sitkan districts, respectively, consists in the great annual range of temperature in the former (57° C. in one known case) as compared with the latter (24°). This uniformity of temperature accompanies humidity everywhere, but I can not see in any case where it alone is accountable for any color characters.

The matter of size is a less conspicuous differential feature of the birds of the interior and coastal regions under consideration, than melanism. Yet in many plastic groups, the representatives in the Yukon district and to a slightly less extent those in the Prince William Sound district, are decidedly larger throughout. The woodpeckers, kinglets, thrushes, and certain finches exhibit this peculiarity. No satisfactory explanation is known to me. The relatively shorter, less pointed wings and shorter tails of the migratory coastal birds appear to be correlated with shorter semi-annual movements. Many of the summer visitants to the Yukon district winter by the way of an interior route far south of the United States, even in South America; while corresponding species in the Sitkan district move south along the Pacific Coast and winter on the Pacific slope of Washington, Oregon, and California. This variation in the shape and area of the wing appears to be, therefore, more obviously adaptive than the melanism.

The Methods and Uses of a Research Museum

THE AVERAGE public museum contains natural history specimens of two categories—those which are displayed within glass cases constantly open to the light, so as to be continually in the view of visitors; and of those which are stored away in various appropriate containers, ordinarily protected from the light, and which are not open for the inspection of the general public, though they may be freely handled and examined by the special student in the field to which they pertain. The former category of specimens constitutes what is usually referred to as the museum proper, or exhibition museum; while the latter forms what may be termed the research museum.

The functions of an exhibition museum have been discussed at length, and its claim to recognition as a valuable factor in public education as well as amusement has been too well established to require further proof. It should be remembered, however, that much of the material on display may at the same time be of direct value in research; for it consists in part of such objects as skeletons which are not affected injuriously by light and which may be encased with a view to easy access by the osteologist who wishes to examine them minutely.

It is in the research department of the museum that I believe lies a great value, even though the sight-seeing visitor may know nothing of its existence. The maintenance of a research department on a large scale is certainly justifiable, as I purpose to show, by the importance of the results to be obtained through it from the standpoint of pure science. In an institution, like the Museum of Vertebrate Zoology, which is an integral part of a large university, it may even be warrantable to emphasize the importance of research over exhibition. For the presence of the research museum serves as a stimulus to the university student and as a source of material and information usable in the work of other departments in the university.

In discussing at length the functions of a research museum, in order to have something concrete to use in illustration, I will refer constantly to the institution with which I am connected. Here, although it has been little more than two years since its inauguration, enough of methods and policies have been formulated to furnish data for the basis of this paper.

The functions of our research department, in other words the energies of our curators and the expenditure of our money allowances, are directed along the following lines:

Our most obvious activity, though not necessarily the most important one, lies in the accumulation of the preservable remains of animals of the vertebrate classes with the exception of those below the Batrachia. I am sure that no one will disagree with me in the claim that the results of our work will be of far greater moment in thus narrowing down the object of our work to a portion of the animal kingdom than if we were to spread it thinly over a greater range of subjects.

The field of our work is the region immediately about us. In other words, it is much less effective to attempt to secure a representation of the animals of the world than to exploit the fauna of a limited area. The Pacific coast is practically inexhaustible, is naturally of easiest access and should be of greatest interest to this institution.

Our collections consist of the skins and skulls of mammals, each individual collected being ordinarily represented by its skin, together, of course, with all dermal structures attached, and the entire skull, cleaned and preserved separately. The entire skeletons of a much smaller proportion of the specimens secured are also preserved; and of the smaller forms the entire animal, a few of each species, is preserved in alcohol for anatomical purposes.

In the class of birds the ordinary study skin is the chief portion preserved. However, the endeavor is made to secure complete skeletons representative of each family at least; and also portions of skeletons of a greater number, consisting of skulls and sterna chiefly. As with the mammals, alcoholic preparations are saved, especially of young birds. The expense and mechanical inconvenience of collecting and storing alcoholics impose a practical limit upon the quantity of material to be cared for in this way.

Reptiles and batrachians are preserved entire as alcoholics. Skeletons should also be prepared and saved, but the difficulty of properly obtaining them has proved so great that as yet we have but few. At any rate, with the entire animal preserved in alcohol it is possible for the special student at any time to take out the skeleton of the reptile or batrachian that it is desired to study.

The museum's policy is, and should be everywhere, liberal as regards the loaning of material to non-resident as well as near-by specialists. Material of any sort is loaned freely to any responsible person any where for the purpose of aiding in his investigations, or as basis of any special study. The value of a museum's hoard of specimens and facts increases in direct ratio to the extent to which they are used. No museum is a success as long as it remains a cold-storage warehouse, closed to ready access by the general student whether he be remotely situated or located within easy reach.

The museum curator only a few years since was satisfied to gather and arrange his research collections with very little reference to their source or to the conditions under which they were obtained. In fact it is surprising to find how little information is on record in regard to collections contained in certain eastern institutions as accessioned previous to about 1885. The modern method, and the one adopted and being carried out more and more in detail by our California museum, is to make the record of each individual acquired, whether it comes in from an outside donor or whether, as is the most usual case, it is secured by the trained museum collector, as complete a history as practicable.

The field collector is supplied with a separate-leaf note-book. He writes his records on the day of observation with carbon ink, on one side of the paper only. The floral surroundings are recorded, especially with respect to their bearing on the animal secured. The behavior of the animal is described and everything else which is thought by the collector to be of use in the study of the species is put on record at the time the observations are made in the field. The camera is as important a part of his outfit as the trap or gun. These field notes and photographs are filed so as to be as readily accessible to the student in the museum as are the specimens themselves.

Furthermore, a rather elaborate system of card cataloguing is maintained in the museum. Three sets of cards, namely, accession, department and reference, which are kept up as a part of the regular work of the curators, enable the enquirer to determine quickly what material is on hand, in what form it is, when and where obtained, and, by following up the cross references to the field note-books, the conditions under which each animal was obtained.

As a matter of routine, each specimen as it is obtained in the field is at once tagged, the label being inscribed in India ink with the exact place of capture, date, collector and field number. The original field number is the same as that under which the animal is at the same time recorded in the field notes. Its original tag is never detached from the specimen, no matter what disposition is made of the latter in arranging the collections in the museum; and so, reversely, the student may quickly trace back again from any particular specimen its history, by referring to the card catalogue and field note-book. In addition to the original collector's number there is added on each label a separate department number by which it is referred to in the museum records and any published articles specifically mentioning it.

It will be observed, then, that our efforts are not merely to accumulate as great a mass of animal remains as possible. On the contrary, we are expending even more time than would be required for the collection of the specimens alone, in rendering what we do obtain as permanently valuable as we know how, to the ecologist as well as the systematist. It is quite probable that the facts of distribution, life history, and economic status may finally prove to be of more far-reaching value, than whatever information is obtainable exclusively from the specimens themselves.

At this point I wish to emphasize what I believe will ultimately prove to be the greatest value of our museum. This value will not, however, be realized until the lapse of many years, possibly a century, assuming that our material is safely preserved. And this is that the student of the future will have access to the original record of faunal conditions in California and the west wherever we now work. He will know the proportional constituency of our faunæ by species, the relative numbers of each species and the extent of the ranges of species as they exist to-day.

Perhaps the most impressive fact brougnt home to the student of geographical distribution, as he carries on his studies, is the profound change that is constantly going on in the faunal make-up of our country. Right now are probably beginning changes to be wrought in the next few years vastly more conspicuous than those that have occurred in ten times that length of time preceding. The effects of deforestation, of tree-planting on the prairies, of the irrigation and cultivation of the deserts, all mean the rapid shifting of faunal boundaries, the extension of ranges of some animals, restriction in the ranges of others, and, with no doubt whatever, the complete extermination of many others, as in a few cases already on record.

If we now had the accurate record of faunal conditions as they were in the Atlantic states a century ago, how much might we not be able to adduce from a study of the changes which have taken place. Now is the opportunity to make such records in our western region. Comparative studies of conditions in the same area at different successive times is bound to bring important generalizations in the field of evolution. It will be seen here how valuable also will prove the collections preserved at corresponding intervals. Changes in conditions will doubtless bring about changes in the habits and physical characters of the animals enduring them.

Another grave danger from the standpoint of the student of natural speciation lies in the introduction of exotic animals. This evil is growing rapidly in the effort to restock regions with more hardy or prolific game animals. If successful from the sportsman's basis, either of two things will happen: the original, native species will become extinct by competitive replacement, or, where the relationships are close, crossing will take place so that the original species will be spoiled through hybridization. There are already instances of both in different sections of the United States. It is highly desirable that a good representation of specimens of the pure, native stock be properly preserved in our museums, for future comparison.

I wish here to register an objection to the prevalent idea that experimental methods upon the higher animals under artificially imposed conditions may be expected to lead invariably to the satisfactory solution of evolutionary problems. I have in mind some experiments recently made upon birds. Certain species were kept captive in enclosures in which a relatively high atmospheric humidity was maintained. The experimenter found that within the life of an individual, in fact within a few months, successive molts resulted in the plumages of some of the birds becoming darker. Feathers which were normally marked lightly with black became solid black. The increase of pigment throughout the plumage brought about a conspicuous change in the appearances of the birds, as great a difference as one finds between two near-related species under natural conditions, the one occupying an area of arid climate, the other a region of humidity.

The conclusion from these few experiments, quite generally, but, I feel confident, too hastily, drawn, has been that there may be a "direct influence" of the atmospheric humidity sufficient to bring about the color characters of the different species as we find them under the varying natural conditions; in other words, that it is not a matter of gradual adaptive acquisition subject to inheritance. It is even being maintained widely among biologists that natural selection may have very little to do with the characters of animals as we find them in nature.

I believe that the above experiments, among others carried on in the same way, will, alone, lead to inductions largely inapplicable to animals in the wild. My chief objection is that wild animals brought into confinement at once begin to show irregularities in various structural respects. This is shown sufficiently by studies upon the skeletons of animals dying in zoological parks, a very large proportion of which are abnormally modified in various particulars. This diseased condition undoubtedly begins just as soon as the animal is taken out of its natural surroundings. For the cessation of any one set of muscular activities is bound to bring about immediate changes in quantitative metabolism in the system. Change in food supply directly affects the entire organism, and unusual invasion by parasites ensues with concomitant irregular growths. How then can we expect to get a knowledge of the processes of species formation under natural conditions from the extraordinary physical development or behavior of such animals?

I would urge that it is only through the close and long-continued study of animals in the wild state, that is, under perfectly natural conditions, that we can hope to gather conclusive evidence as to the causes and methods of evolution. Our research museum has assumed the rôle of recorder of faunal conditions as they are in this age. I reiterate, for emphasis, that I believe its greatest ultimate value will not, therefore, be fully realized until a later period.

But to return to our immediate activities and their justification: The mass of information already at hand brings us face to face with numerous problems of distribution and variation. As our field work is carried on, we learn more and more in detail of the extent of the range of each species of animal, and we are able to recognize more clearly the correlated factors. We are able with more accuracy to define the characters of the local races or subspecies. The study of these "small species" I believe is leading to a better understanding of the relationships of animals and the causes of evolution than if we ignored the slight varieties and contented ourselves with dealing systematically only with the species differentiated so far as to be distinguishable at a glance.

Systematists, either as members of our museum staff or students from elsewhere, who make use of our material, are putting on published record the more important facts of distribution and variation as they come to light. All of this activity leads to the more thorough knowledge of animals necessary for any sort of wider generalization. Our institution is a repository of facts; and no matter what may be said to the contrary by those who undervalue the efforts of the hoarder of facts, it must always be the mass of carefully ascertained facts upon which the valid generalization rests. I have lately learned from no less than three zoologists of prominence that the published scientific paper which does not include some induction or generalization is not worth while. The result, it seems to me, of such a sentiment as this, which is being promulgated among the younger students, is to encourage premature conclusions. The object, in the view of the young research student, becomes the discovery of generalizations, and he is liable to be content with a wholly insufficient basis of facts. We can not expect satisfactory inductions from scanty data any sooner than from inaccurate data. At the same time I do realize that the ultimate value of the facts lies in their service as indicators of general truths. The amassing of detailed facts in any field of science is certainly a commendable pursuit; and if generalizations of wide application are early indicated, so much the better. Our research museum is a repository of facts.

There is a more widely-appreciated function of our institution which is already asserting itself as an important one in the research museum's activities, especially in its connection with a state university: People want to know whether or not a reptile is poisonous; whether or not a bird is beneficial or injurious; whether or not a "wild animal" is to be feared. People instinctively want to know the names of things. There is the mere curiosity, perfectly laudable, which brings such questions as these to the museum in greater and greater number. It is as a popular source of information that no small part of the curator's time is occupied.

The economic value of birds and mammals to the agricultural interests of the state is one of practical importance. In our field work we obtain a great amount of information applicable along this line; and, further, our staff keeps posted as to the results of the important work carried on by our national government to ascertain the beneficial or injurious effects of wild animals. Either from knowledge acquired directly by ourselves, or from that published elsewhere, we are often able to give the information asked for. The museum is thus constituted a popular bureau of information as regards the higher vertebrate animals of the region with which we are familiar.

The functions of a research museum may be summarized as follows: Collecting and preserving animals of certain groups from a limited region; recording in permanent form all obtainable information in regard to their distribution, variation, economic status and habits; serving as a bureau of popular information as regards the animals of the region worked in; the description and analysis of ecologic and faunal conditions as they are to-day; the publication of the immediately important data obtained, calling attention to whatever generalizations these facts may point towards.

The Colorado River
as a Highway of Dispersal and
Center of Differentiation
of Species

ACCORDING to Gilbert and Scofield (1898, pp. 487, 488) the peculiarities of the fish fauna of the Colorado River bespeak a very long period of absolute isolation. A remarkably high percentage of its fishes are specifically distinct from those of the other river basins of western North America. The same is to be said of the riparian birds and mammals.

So far as known to the present writer, none of the species listed with a star in the following table ranges beyond the confines of the Colorado River basin, including of course its various tributaries and distributaries such as the Gila and New rivers, except sporadically, or as accounted for by distal invasion through passes or along seacoastal tracts. In other words, the Colorado River has been in existence so long that the conditions imposed by its presence have figured in the differentiation of representative species of several families, both mammalian and avian.

The great age of the Colorado River is indicated geologically by the vast extent and slow rate of the erosion involved in the formation of the Grand Cañon. This time-element is justly inferred to have been an essential condition in the formation of these species.

It may not be amiss to consider these riparian species somewhat with regard to origin. By confining our attention to the north-and-south valley of the lower Colorado, this becomes, with a knowledge of the general status in North America of each group represented, a comparatively simple matter. The axiom holds, that, because of the ever-shifting location geographically of associational, faunal and zonal conditions, every single element or line of descent, now represented in the biota of any one locality must have come either in its present form or in some antecedent one from somewhere else. This is certainly true of all terrestrial life. Elevation and depression have worked like a seesaw in dislocating faunas. The Colorado valley is a trough, hemmed in associationally on either side, and only capable of influx of riparian elements at either end. Therefore the riparian species of the Colorado fauna can have entered the area under consideration from only two directions: from the north and from the south.

SPECIES WHICH BELONG TO THE RIPARIAN BELT, AND WHICH ARE THEREFORE
HEMMED IN BY THE PARALLELING DESERT TRACTS. STARRED SPECIES
ARE PECULIAR TO THE COLORADO SUBFAUNA

BREEDING BIRDS	MAMMALS
Agelaius phoeniceus sonoriensis*	Castor canadensis frondator*
Melospiza melodia saltonis*	Peromyscus maniculatus sonoriensis
Pipilo aberti*	Sigmodon hispidus eremicus*
Guiraca caerulea lazula	Reithrodontomys megalotis deserti
Piranga rubra cooperi	Neotoma albigula venusta*
Vireo belli arizonae*	Ondatra zibethica pallida*
Vermivora luciae*	Mephitis estor
Dendroica aestiva sonorana*	Procyon pallidus*
Toxostoma crissale*	

Only two species are clearly seen to have entered the Colorado valley from the north: *Castor canadensis frondator,* and *Ondatra zibethica pallida.* The following species or subspecies are believed to have come in from the south: *Pipilo aberti, Guiraca caerulea lazula, Piranga rubra cooperi, Vireo belli arizonae, Vermivora luciae, Toxostoma crissale, Sigmodon hispidus eremicus, Neotoma albigula venusta.*

In the remaining seven cases (*Agelaius, Melospiza, Dendroica, Peromyscus, Reithrodontomys, Mephitis* and *Procyon*) no grounds are apparent to the writer for assigning either one over the other direction of invasion, and this in spite of whatever may be the marked Austral or Boreal distributional affinities of each group concerned. The tide of invasion may in fact in these species have tended in one direction at one period, in the opposite at another; or, as in *Peromyscus maniculatus sonoriensis,* the Colorado valley may have acted continuously as a narrow bridge where have met and mingled descent-lines from both the north and the south.

The obvious fact that southern representatives prevail over northern ones is clearly attributable to the present zonal condition obtaining in the region, namely Austral, in its Lower Sonoran division. And evidence elsewhere assembled (Grinnell and Swarth, 1913, p. 383) points towards an increasing temperature throughout the region. This would result in decreasing the favorableness to Boreal forms and increasing the availability of the region for immigration of Austral types. Consideration of the xerophilous vertebrates as well as of the riparian ones leaves little doubt in the writer's mind but that this has been the actual course of events. The northern contingent is on the wane, the southern in the ascendency.

The query presents itself: is the Colorado fauna *full?* Are all the ecological niches, which are available in this area and which have occupants in other regions, occupied here? Probably not, for the intervention of barriers has doubtless prevented the invasion of types which, if they could have once gotten there, would have thriven and assumed a place as endemic elements in the fauna. Sporadic incursion, as of migrants among birds, and strays among both birds and mammals, do not appear to the writer to figure in such a process. Rather must it be a progressive invasion of the species *en masse,* acquiring, it may be, adaptive modifications at it proceeds. In other words, the conquering of the land is the combined result of the facilities offered by it plus the relative amenability of each species concerned.

The twelve riparian species and subspecies peculiar to the Colorado fauna vary much in degree of difference from their near relatives which occupy adjacent differentiation areas. These varying degrees of difference might be interpreted as measures of the periods of time elapsed since the entrance into the region of each of the types involved. That this conclusion is poorly grounded is evident upon consideration of the various other elements which must figure in the process of species formation. Among these may be suggested: degree of isolation, divergence of homologous associational conditions in the new region from those in the ancestral, and inherent susceptibility to adaptive modification in each of the species concerned.

In the problem of the origin of the riparian portion of the Colorado fauna we seem to have to do with an accentuated kind of isolation. For, as already asserted, there is such a thing as *more* and *less* isolation. In the region here considered, possessing extreme associational contrast, we find the ordinary geographic, or more properly speaking, physiographic, isolation coupled with associational isolation. In consequence of this extra favorable contingency, differentiation of species may have progressed with particular celerity, with such distinct forms to show for it as *Pipilo aberti, Vermivora luciae, Toxostoma crissale,* and *Procyon pallidus.*

The axiom has presented itself in this connection that the *more* restricted a species is associationally, that is, the more confined to a narrow range of associational conditions, the more subject it is to the important factor of isolation; hence the more liable to give rise to new incipient strains in different parts of its general range.

An assertion which seems at first glance opposed to the above is: that the *less* restricted a species is associationally, that is, the more *widely* adaptable to varying conditions, the more numerous the chances for local operation of isolation, because more opportunity for radial dispersion to carry the species into distant localities and under extreme conditions, and for the ultimate interposition of more or less efficient barriers. The factor of distance might here replace the operation of associational restriction in segregating descent-line plexuses.

These are apparently incongruous notions, but the following conception tends to harmonize them; namely, that, granting the three totally different orders of distributionally limiting factors (zonal, faunal and associational), it is probable that different species are restricted *unevenly* with respect to the three; thus a certain wood-rat (*Neotoma intermedia desertorum*) is restricted faunally, but ranges widely through zones and associations; a certain wren (*Telmatodytes palustris* and subspecies) is tightly restricted associationally, but ranges widely through faunas and zones; a xerophilous genus of rodents (*Perognathus*) is closely restricted zonally and associationally, but ranges rather widely as to fauna. So that both the above assertions might well be true of a single animal historically and even, in different parts of its range, simultaneously! Certainly the first serves in explanation of the multiplicity of geographic races or species in several widespread groups of birds and mammals.

The Colorado River as a Hindrance to the Dispersal of Species

BATS AND most birds find in the Colorado River no hindrance whatever to individual travel. Freedom of aerial locomotion gives them superiority over any obstruction on the general level of the country they inhabit. It is possible that in a few of the resident birds of limited flight individuals do not regularly cross the main stream, though they readily could do so if such an exigency as that of fire sweeping the bottom lands should drive them to it. *Geococcyx californianus, Pipilo aberti* and *Toxostoma crissale* are birds which probably do not often cross the river under normal circumstances.

Among mammals, carnivores are usually of much wider foraging range than rodents. From all the data available it appears that none of the carnivores, not even the cats, are averse to swimming the river if need be. Among rodents, however, our work showed a number of cases in which the Colorado River had effectively checked the distribution of species. The following tables show the situation as regards all the rodents of the region (see also figs. A, B).*

The fact is apparent that only members of the strictly desert associations are stopped at the river. And of these the species of the *most remote associational position* are, with one exception, *Neotoma intermedia desertorum,* most effectively delimited. Also *degree of isolation* is in a measure commensurate with *amount of difference* between forms of the same genus.

It is pertinent to inquire *how* the Colorado River acts as a barrier to those species affected. It appears that in every one of the eleven cases the animal in question has no need to visit any water-supply. All are species capable of maintaining suc-

---

* The tables are on page 48, here. The figures are omitted.

RODENTS IN WHICH THE COLORADO RIVER ACTS AS AN ABSOLUTE BARRIER

Association	Arizona side		California side	Association
Encelia and Rocky Creosote	{ Ammospermophilus harrisi harrisi		Ammospermophilus leucurus leucurus }	Encelia and Rocky Creosote
			Peromyscus crinitus stephensi }	Encelia
Sandy Creosote {	Thomomys chrysonotus	Colorado River		
			Thomomys albatus }	Saltbush
			Perognathus formosus }	Encelia and Rocky Creosote
Encelia and Rocky Creosote {	Perognathus intermedius			
			Perognathus spinatus spinatus }	Encelia and Rocky Creosote

RODENTS WHICH OCCUR ON BOTH SIDES OF THE COLORADO RIVER, BUT WHICH SHOW SLIGHT, ALMOST IMPALPABLE, DIFFERENCES ON THE TWO SIDES

	Association
Citellus tereticaudus tereticaudus	Sandy Creosote and Saltbush
Dipodomys deserti deserti	Sandy Creosote and Saltbush
Perognathus penicillatus penicillatus	Saltbush and Sandy Creosote

RODENTS WHICH ARE APPARENTLY IDENTICAL ON THE TWO SIDES OF THE COLORADO RIVER

	Association
Castor canadensis frondator	River
Peromyscus maniculatus sonoriensis	All Riparian
Peromyscus eremicus eremicus	Saltbush and Sandy Creosote
Sigmodon hispidus eremicus	Willow and Tule
Reithrodontomys megalotis deserti	Tule and Willow
Neotoma albigula venusta	Mesquite and other Riparian
Neotoma intermedia desertorum	Encelia
Ondatra zibethica pallida	River
Dipodomys merriami merriami	Saltbush and Sandy Creosote
Perognathus bombycinus	Sandy Creosote
Lepus californicus deserticola	Creosote and Saltbush
Sylvilagus auduboni arizonae	Quailbrush and Mesquite

cessful existence without a drop of water other than that obtained by chemical elaboration from their food. In our three months' experience we did not once find evidence that any individual of any of the eleven species in question had visited the river's edge.

Furthermore, to the best of our knowledge, all the species are of limited foraging range. In the case of the two diurnal chipmunks, *Ammospermophilus harrisi harrisi* and *Ammospermophilus leucurus leucurus,* which could be *seen,* it was seldom that an individual was come upon more than fifty yards from its burrow. In the case of *Perognathus,* which carefully closes the mouths of its burrows for the day, after its night's activity abroad, it was impossible to secure definite information on this score except as afforded by trapping; but the writer's impression is that it, too, does not ordinarily venture many rods from its retreat. Individuals doubtless travel farther at times of rutting, but it is likely that even then the limits of the native association would not be far transgressed.

It is further to be noted that those species finding an insuperable check at the river are all closely confined to one general kind of associational environment, even though two minor associations, as here defined, be occupied. The river *plus* intervening associations of an unfavorable nature constitutes the *total* barrier to the rodents in question.

It is true that the element of distance here implied is reduced to a negligible quantity where hills closely abut upon the river channel. But the major part of the river's course, probably four-fifths of it below the lower end of the Grand Cañon, is through valleys of varying width, occupied by riparian associations most adverse in essential ecological particulars to the species of the upland deserts adjacent.

Along the remaining fifth of the river's course, where the banks rise abruptly and are continuous with the adjacent hill slopes, with either no trace of riparian tracts or only narrow or interrupted representations, it would seem that chance *is* afforded for such mammals as the desert chipmunks and pocket mice to encounter the river itself, with all intervening factors removed.

At our base camp (no. 4) at The Needles, our measurements showed the actual width of the stream to be 450 feet at the rather low stage of water obtaining at that time (March 4, 1910). At high water the river could not have been much more than 150 feet wider (see sectional profile, fig. A, and pl. 10, fig. 15).* In the box cañon two to three miles below, the width of the river *appeared* to be much less, and, because of the precipitous walls, high water would make little change in width.

The two species of *Ammospermophilus* were *seen* at points only about 850 feet apart in a direct line. All the mammals of the Encelia association, as segregated here on the two sides of the river, were trapped at this station within one thousand feet of one another. The same situation obviously held at several other points along the Colorado River. The sharp separation of the ranges of nearly related vertebrates by a barrier of such narrow width is, to the best of the writer's knowledge, not known elsewhere in North America.

As to the opportunities for crossing the river by such individuals as might get to the water's edge, only speculation is now possible. At times of rising water, riparian mammals are undoubtedly often marooned upon islands and finally forced to swim or to take refuge on floating drift. Practically all the riparian species are known to be able to swim readily, and are probably in ways just mentioned frequently carried from side to side of the river.

The ability of typical desert animals to care for themselves if cast into the water is problematical, though a little experimentation would go far to proving the point one way or the other. Their powers in this line may be inferred to be limited because of the facilities normally lacking for putting such powers into practice. For instance, there is fair probability that a *Reithrodontomys* could safely cross a turbulent stretch of current, where a *Perognathus* would perish before any chance of reaching the shore.

---

* Illustrations omitted.

Protracted observation along the river brings conviction to the observer that no animal of weak swimming powers is likely to survive many minutes of exposure to the main current. It is a fascinating diversion to watch the course of a stick or log adrift in the stream. Such an object pursues an exceedingly devious course. It may be carried close under the steep outside bank of an ox-bow swing, only to be directly thrown back towards the opposite shore. Stretches of rough water may be encountered where the object is swamped at the crest of every wave. Or, along rocky parts of the channel, swirls, large and small, arrest its passage. In the most violent of these eddies a twenty-foot log was seen to up-end and sink from sight, to reappear after its total submergence, a hundred yards down stream.

At times of falling water a great deal of drift lodges on mudbars and projecting reefs of rock. It is imaginable that drift logs *might* be reached by individuals, which freed again with subsequently rising water, would carry their passengers until lodged under favoring circumstances on the opposite side of the river. In the account of *Neotoma intermedia desertorum,* the only rodent of the Encelia association not checked by the river, it is suggested that in some such way passage was secured from the California to the Arizona side of the river. This wood rat now bids fair to occupy much appropriate territory in southwestern Arizona not previously possessing an associational homologue, that is a Neotoman representative. *Neotoma* may be looked upon as a more hardy and ecologically less specialized rodent than any of its associational companions. It is certainly much the largest, and is notoriously of aggressive disposition as a forager.

Of the eight species of delimited rodents, not one individual of the hundreds trapped was found on the "wrong" side of the river. As far as they went, then, our efforts furnished no evidence that even an occasional individual does get across. As already shown, there seems to be nothing to attract the upland rodents to the water's edge, so that possibility of securing safe transportation on a log or mass of drift is doubly remote. Now, supposing that a single individual *did* manage to reach the opposite shore, its *species* would not necessarily be established there. In most cases (not, however, with *Peromyscus crinitus stephensi* and *Perognathus formosus*) there is already established an associational homologue, with which even a whole family of the invaders would have to compete, with the chances at least as much against success as favoring it. Hybridization might occur, granted that no sexual antipathy arise, but, whatever the immediate results, it is the impression of the writer that swamping would eventually be likely to wipe out all trace of the invading species. This impression is admittedly based upon fragmentary data which has not been subjected to critical analysis. Whether or not Mendelian behavior in inheritance of characters obtains among the rodents here concerned is yet to be proven.

Suffice it to say that all the evidence at hand shows the Colorado River to have effectually blocked distribution, in the two directions concerned in the eight cases as listed. While this hindrance to distribution involves the species, it does so through its mechanical action upon the frontier *individuals* of each species. Hypothetically the invaders are severally hurled back or else destroyed outright.

The divergent characters displayed by the upland rodents of the two sides of the Colorado River are, in the mind of the writer, to be best explained on historical grounds. It is not necessary to believe that the specific characters concerned arose in the immediate vicinity of the river, though the circumstance of segregation alone is deemed by some to suffice as a cause of differentiation. The climatic features (zonal and faunal, as well as associational) are identical on the two sides of the river. Rather is it reasonable to presuppose separate and rather remote centers of differentiation, and convergent dispersal through time and space which brought the resulting types to the verge of the river, beyond which they were unable to spread.

It is possible that an arm of the sea continuous with the Gulf of California once extended northward into southern Nevada. A submergence of only 1,000 feet would divide the present desert areas of western Arizona and southern California into two peninsular land masses, which might have served as well-isolated centers of differentiation for various forms which later spread with the elevation of the land until their ranges abutted. Unfortunately for this suggestion, as I am informed by Professor John C. Merriam, geological evidence fails so far to show the existence of such conditions within Pleistocene or even Pliocene times. The suggested explanation must therefore be discarded in our dealing with the differentiation of present-day species and subspecies, especially since even the genera represented and as now restricted are not known to have evolved so early as Miocene.

But another process, recognizable far and wide in dynamic zoo-geography, may be called into account without assuming any departure in the past from topographic and climatic conditions as they are today. Comparison of the fauna of the Lower Sonoran plains of south central Arizona with that of the Mohave desert plateau in the same zone, shows two prevalent character combinations among the nearly related component species. The mid-Arizona representatives are usually dark colored and large sized, the reverse appearing to hold in the majority of the Mohave desert forms. There is considerable floral difference in the two regions, and minor climatic differences are well known. Different environments thus impinge upon the animals in these widely separated centers, and more or less regular blending of conditions occurs between. Although every factor of environment may be identical immediately on the two sides of the Colorado River, the animals now there have undoubtedly descended from ancestral lines which have invaded the territory from the two opposite directions, bringing with them by inheritance the characters developed under the two different sets of conditions.

To express the idea otherwise, from each differentiation

area there is an outwardly radiating dispersal of descent-lines, involving time as well as space. This dispersive process is going on now as it has through past time. The eastward-flowing tide of Mohave forms would only be arrested by an insuperable barrier, such as the Colorado River. The westward invading descent-lines from the Arizona center would proceed until stopped by the same barrier. Both sets of forms would find themselves along the Colorado Valley under the same associational, faunal and zonal conditions; but each set is continually receiving by the process of inheritance plus invasion the peculiar characters generated on its own side.

While the Colorado River probably lies in an intermediate position between the Mohave and Arizona faunas, the area of intermediate conditions of environment is probably relatively narrow. This very element of narrowness may be called into account for the lack of modification displayed by the delimited species of the Colorado River frontiers, for example, in the case of *Ammospermophilus*.

Supposing now that the Colorado River does not serve as an insuperable barrier, nor ever has done so; invasion would have extended from one side to the other as far as associational, faunal or zonal barriers permitted. In animals of wide distribution, intergradation geographically between the remote extremes would in the end be expected to occur. The extremes would not then have differentiated so far, at least in quantity of each character developed, because of inheritance from the opposite type, again involving time and space, concomitantly. Subspecies would have resulted, instead of full species. This condition doubtless obtains in some of the birds, as well as in some of the rodents listed as being the same on the two sides of the river. Take, as an example, *Dipodomys merriami merriami* of south central Arizona, and *Dipodomys merriami simiolus* of the Mohave desert. Our Colorado River series is fairly intermediate between the extreme types, though the extremes are not so different as are *Ammospermophilus harrisi harrisi* and *Ammospermophilus leucurus leucurus*. As elsewhere explained, the river is believed to be not so much of a barrier to *Dipodomys merriami* as to the forms of *Ammospermophilus*.

The *degree of hindrance,* ranging from the condition, as in the case of *Castor* and *Ondatra,* where the river offers no bar to perfect freedom of crossing, to that where the river is an absolute barrier, as in the case of species of *Perognathus* and *Ammospermophilus,* accords so closely with *degree of difference* in characters developed on the two sides of the river, that adequate ground is afforded for the belief that intervention of barriers is a prime factor in the differentiation of species. And furthermore, it would appear that no two species, in birds and mammals, arise except through geographic segregation.

Barriers to Distribution
as Regards Birds and Mammals

THE GEOGRAPHICAL RANGE of any species of animal may be likened to a reservoir of water in a mountain canyon. The confining walls are of varying nature. A concrete dam, absolutely impervious, may retain the water at one end. Along either side the basin's walls differ in consistency from place to place. The substratum varies in porosity, at some points being impervious like the dam, at others permitting of seepage of water to a greater or less distance from the main volume. The water continually presses against its basin walls, as if seeking to enlarge its area. And it may succeed in escaping, by slow seepage through such portions of its barrier as are pervious or soluble, or by free flow through a gap in the walls, if such offers. The area occupied by the water will extend itself most rapidly along the lines of least resistance.

Every species has a center or centers of abundance in which favoring conditions usually give rise to a rate of reproduction more than sufficient to keep the critical area stocked. A tendency to occupy a larger space results, because of competition within the species: individuals and descent-lines multiply and travel radially, extending those portions of the frontier where least resistance is offered. Such radial dispersal takes place slowly in some directions, more rapidly in others, according to the degree of passability of the opposing barriers. These barriers consist of any sort of conditions less favorable to the existence of the species than those in the center of abundance.

Theoretically, sooner or later and in all directions, every species is absolutely stopped. But as a matter of undoubted fact most barriers are continually shifting, and the adaptability of the animals themselves may be also undergoing continual modification; so that perfect adjustment is beyond the limits of possibility so long as topography and climate keep changing. The ranges of species may thus be constantly shifting. Descent-lines may move about repeatedly over the same general region, like sparks in the soot on the back of a brick fireplace.

Yet, in all of our studies, of but a few years' duration, the time element is reduced almost to a negligible quantity, and we may look upon the areas occupied by each species as, for the time of our observation, fixed. We are thus enabled to compare one with another, and because of the large number of the species, we can infer a good deal as to the nature of barriers in general, at least as regards birds and mammals. It is even conceivable that, with sufficient refinement in methods, the inquirer might in time find himself able, from a comparative study of the ranges of rodents, for example, to establish the identity of all of the external factors which have to do with the persistence of each of the species; in other words to analyze the "environmental complex" into its uttermost elements—as regards the existing species of rodents in their recent development.

The most obvious kind of barrier to distribution is that consisting of any sort of physical, or mechanical, obstruction. Such obstruction affects directly the *individuals* of a species encountering it, either by stopping their advance or by destroying outright such as attempt to cross it. As barriers of this nature, are to be cited land in the case of purely aquatic mammals, and bodies of water to purely terrestrial, especially xerophilous, mammals. In each case the width of the barrier has to do with the degree of impassability. Oceans and continents are most perfect, and affect a large proportion of the species. The comparatively narrow Colorado River is a barrier of the first rank, but only to a certain few desert rodents. Mechanical barriers, where they exist at all, are clearly recognizable.

It is to be observed, however, upon considering the birds and mammals of a whole continent, that by far the greater number of species are delimited in range without any reference to actual land and water boundaries; more explicitly, their ranges fall far short of coast lines. The barriers here concerned are intangible, but nevertheless powerful. By their action the spread of species, genera and families is held in check as surely as by any tangible obstruction.

By these invisible barriers the *individual* may not necessarily be stopped at all, as with animals of free locomotion; but the *species* is affected. For example, the mocking bird in its Californian distribution is closely confined to those parts of the state possessing certain definite climatic features; but vagrant individuals, especially in autumn, occur far beyond the limits of these restrictive conditions. Carnivorous mammals are well known to be subject to sporadic wanderings on the part of individuals, but the *species* is kept in set bounds by some potent but invisible set of factors. The very fact that *individuals* are quite capable of temporarily transgressing these bounds and yet do not overstep them *en masse* emphasizes all the more the remarkable potency of this category of barriers as regards species and higher groups.

Our geographic studies lead us to designate among these relatively intangible barriers: (1) increase or decrease in prevailing temperature beyond certain critical limits, according to the species concerned; (2) increase or decrease in prevailing atmospheric humidity beyond certain limits; (3) modification in food-supply and appropriate breeding and foraging ground. The limits set by each of these factors will vary with the physiological peculiarities of the organism considered; in other words the inherent structural equipment of each animal figures importantly. In these three sorts of barriers will be recognized what have been called *"zonal," "faunal,"* and *"associational"* delimitation, each of which I will now try to define.

Two schools of faunistic students are represented among American zoo-geographic writers of the present day. One, of which C. H. Merriam is the most prominent exponent, sees in temperature the chief cause controlling distribution, and deals with the ranges of species in terms of "life zones." The other school, of which C. C. Adams, A. G. Ruthven and Spencer Trotter are active advocates, assigns to temperature but a minor

rôle, looking rather to a composite control, of many factors, resulting in ecologic "associations," of which plants are essential
elements, and which are to be further explained on historical
grounds. The two sets of areas thus defined do not by any means
correspond. Yet the reviewer can not fail to note, here and
there, places where boundaries coincide, and such coincidences
are so frequent as to be suggestive of real concordance in some
significant manner. Is it not probable that both schools are approximately correct, the difference in mode of treatment being
due to different weights given the different kinds of evidence,
or, in other words, to difference in perspective?

Every animal is believed to be limited in distribution zonally
by greater or less degree of temperature, more particularly by
that of the reproductive season. When a number of animals
(always in company with many plants similarly restricted) approximately agree in such limitation they are said to occupy
the same life zone.

The observation of this category of distributional delimitation is particularly easy in an area of great altitudinal diversity
like that comprised in the southwestern United States. The
writer is led to wonder if those authors who minimize the importance of temperature have ever been privileged to travel
extensively, and *carry on field studies,* outside of the relatively
uniform eastern half of North America!

Study of any area which varies widely in altitude and hence
provides readily appreciable differences in daily temperature
from place to place brings conviction of the very great effectiveness of temperature in delimiting the ranges of nearly all
species of animals as well as of plants. Particular attention may
be called to the pertinent results of Merriam's survey of Mount
Shasta.

But temperature is not to be considered the only delimiting
factor of environment, though its possible overemphasis by the
Merriam school seems to have led some other persons to believe
that this view is held. In fact it becomes evident, after a consideration of appropriate data, that very many species are kept

within geographic bounds in certain directions only by an increasing or decreasing degree of atmospheric *humidity*. By plotting the ranges of many animals as well as of plants coincidence in this regard is found in so many cases as to warrant the recognition of a number of "faunal areas"—on the causative basis of relative uniformity in humidity. It is probable that every species is affected by both orders of geographic control.

The reader may enquire as to the grounds for employing the widely used terms zone and fauna in the restricted sense here prescribed. In reply, it may be said that this is not an innovation, but is an adoption of a usage which has come about historically among a certain group of workers in the geography of vertebrate animals in North America. The writer recognizes the fault in imposing restricted meanings upon old terms, but he also hesitates at coining new words.

As to which is *the more* important, assembled data seem to show that more genera and higher groups are delimited by zonal boundaries than by faunal boundaries. The arresting power of temperature barriers would therefore seem to be relatively the greater.

In the third category of distributional control there is a conspicuous association of the majority of so-called adaptive structures of animals (often of high taxonomic value) with certain mechanical, or physical, features of their environment. An animal may thus intimately depend upon certain inorganic or organic peculiarities, or both, of a given area, and be unable to maintain existence beyond the limits of occurrence of those features of the environment. Tracts of relatively uniform environmental conditions, including their inanimate as well as living elements, are here called *associations*.

After a consideration of all the birds and mammals occurring both within the state of California and elsewhere as far as the writer's knowledge goes, associational restriction appears to be governed by the following three factors, of relative importance in the order named.

1. Kind of food-supply afforded, with regard to the inherent

structural powers of each of the animals concerned to make it available.

2. Presence of safe breeding places, adapted to the varying needs of the animals, in other words depending upon the respective inherent powers of construction, defence and concealment in each species concerned.

3. Presence of places of temporary refuge for individuals, during daytime or nighttime, or, while foraging, when hard-pressed by predatory enemies, again correlated with the respective inherent powers of defence and concealment of each species involved.

CLASSIFICATION OF BARRIERS TO SPECIES AS REGARDS BIRDS AND MAMMALS

Barriers:

A. Intangible.

    (*a'*) Zonal (by temperature).

    (*b'*) Faunal (by atmospheric humidity).

    (*c'*) Associational.

        (1) By food supply.

        (2) By breeding places.

        (3) By temporary refuges.

           (Each of these three with regard to the inherent structural characters of each species concerned.)

B. Tangible (mechanical).

    (*a''*) Land to aquatic species.

    (*b''*) Bodies or streams of water to terrestrial species.

It is believed that the geographical distribution of any animal is correctly diagnosed in terms of each of the three main groupings here suggested. In other words an animal belongs simultaneously to one or more zones, to one or more faunas, and to one or more associations. No one of these groupings can be stated in terms of the other, any more than a person can compute liquids by candle-power, or weight in miles. The constituent species within each of these groupings always belong to the other two. To illustrate: the southern white-headed woodpecker inhabits the coniferous forest association of the San Bernardino fauna of the Transition zone; the Abert towhee belongs to the mesquite and the quail-brush associations of the Colorado Desert fauna, of the Lower Sonoran zone; the Pacific shrew belongs to the upland riparian association of the northern coast redwood fauna of the Transition and Boreal zones.

The above categories are believed to include all the factors commonly involved in checking the spread of species of birds and mammals. It is possible that inter-specific competition may sometimes occur where associational homologues meet. But even here it becomes a matter of relative associational fitness which determines supremacy and consequent ultimate limits of invasion of the forms concerned.

A mountain range, mechanically speaking, is no barrier at all, *per se,* as frequently alleged. Only as it involves zonal or faunal barriers does it affect distribution. The same is true of a valley or a desert.

As far as contemplation of cases has gone, the writer's experience has led him to believe that the outlines of the ranges of all birds and mammals may be accounted for by one or more of the factors indicated in the analysis here presented. And as detailed knowledge of the facts of geographical distribution accumulates, the delimiting factors become more and more readily detectable. By such a study, of *comparative distribution,* it seems possible that the ranges of birds and mammals may become subject to satisfactory explanation.

When considered in its historical bearing, the problem of barriers concerns itself intimately with the origin of species. It is believed by the writer that only through the agency of barriers is the *multiplication of species,* in birds and mammals, brought about.

The present contribution is abbreviated from a general discussion of certain distributional problems which forms part of a paper to appear from the University of California press and which treats in detail of the birds and mammals of the lower Colorado Valley, in California and Arizona.

Conserve the Collector

IT IS WITH considerable apprehension that I have observed an unmistakable decrease in the number of collectors during the past six or eight years. Matters of precision and accuracy in the field of ornithology are, I have no doubt, suffering as a consequence of this forsaking of the "shotgun method." Our faunistic literature to be of the highest scientific character must be based on the surest means of establishing the identification of species. The "skin record" is essential, and the availability of this is dependent upon the existence and activity of the collector.

The type of field observer who depends solely on long-range identification is becoming more and more prevalent. But the opera-glass student, even if experienced, can not be depended upon to take the place of the collector. Accuracy in identification of species and especially subspecies rests for final appeal upon the actual capture and comparison of specimens. Ornithology as a science is threatened, and it should not be allowed to lapse wholly into the status of a recreation or a hobby, to be indulged in only in a superficial way by amateurs or dilettantes.

It is to be doubted whether authoritative and expert systematic and field ornithologists can be developed through any other process than by personal collecting of adequate numbers of specimens in the field. The processes of hunting, and personal preparation of bird skins, bring a knowledge of the characters of birds, both in life and as pertaining to their structure and plumage, which can be secured in no other way.

The present tendency toward extermination of the collector bears obvious close relationship to the increasing number of extreme sentimentalists. The latter, beginning in a good cause, now continue to urge stringency in state and federal laws beyond all reason. Those in authority "high up" ought to know better than to contribute to this stringency; but they, yielding to the pressure of the militant sentimentalists, are allowing laws and regulations to go through without giving apparently any thought to their duty toward the field naturalist, whose function is essential to the conduct of important phases of ornithological study.

Permits should be issued by both state and federal governments freely to applicants upon avowed sincerity of purpose. There should be no hesitation unless there be suspicion as to the honesty of the applicant. Limitations may be properly imposed, as, for instance, by excepting rare or disappearing species like the ivory-billed woodpecker or the Carolina parakeet. This is just as feasible as it is to forbid the sportsman to shoot rare or disappearing game species. Furthermore, the collector, by reason of his more expert knowledge, is far better able to discriminate between closely allied species, and, because of his appreciation of the facts upon which the principles of conservation are based, is more likely to abstain from killing the wholly protected species. As a rule, the birds which particularly interest the collector consist of small species, of wide distribution and large numbers. And the daily "bag-limit" of the collector, self-imposed because of the subsequent labor entailed, is small, seldom exceeding 20 birds all told, and, in my own experience, averaging 12.

Collecting, at best, will be indulged in by but comparatively few people, for it involves much more effort than hunting; the successful collector must possess a considerable equipment in the way of industry and artistic skill if he expects to reach recognized standing in the fraternity of collecting ornithologists; and at the outset he must possess the naturalist's gift or "bent" which is itself not common.

It can be rightly urged in this connection that the justification for collecting non-game birds is just as well grounded as for shooting or otherwise destroying *game* animals. Practically all small birds can better stand an annual toll than most game birds. Citing a single species of non-game bird, the Audubon warbler, I believe that its numbers within the state of California at the beginning of the winter season exceed the combined numbers of all the species of game birds within the state at the beginning of the open season. Yet for the pursuit of game birds over one hundred and thirty thousand hunting licenses were issued last year here in California alone. In the same state, only one hundred permits for scientific collecting were allowed, or only one permit to collect non-game birds to 1,300 licenses to hunt game birds! Most of these permits were limited to two specimens of a kind, and in many cases they were given out grudgingly or under protest, as if the collector were seeking something beyond his rights to ask for, or even as if a question of morality were involved! This again is an attitude (on the part of *sportsmen,* which our State Game Commissioners all are!) hardly consistent, but evidently resulting from the widespread influence of the sentimentalist.

As compared with the value of the game birds shot, does not the bird killed for a specimen come much more nearly justifying its end? The game bird practically ends its career of usefulness when it falls before the gun. It has incited recreation and a certain amount of the esthetic in the way of admiration. Perhaps the latter obtains for a few minutes or hours after the death of the bird. But it soon goes to pot and that is the end of it.

With the bird hunted for a specimen, the collector is searching discriminatingly among many species and often among a great many individuals. He is observing many things beyond the mere object of the shot. In addition, full recreative value is being obtained as in the case of game (and this is generally urged now-a-days as *the* value of game—in its service, not as food, but as an object of pursuit and contemplation before killing). The value of a bird shot for a specimen does not end with its death, although it has served the other functions already. The collector prepares the bird with painstaking care, at the same time acquiring added information, and installs it under safe conditions as an object of study and appreciation for all time. Instead of being merely eaten, it becomes a joy forever.

To my mind, there is no more practical reason for shooting a snipe for sport than for shooting a Savannah sparrow for a specimen.

My thesis is, not that hunting game for sport is unjustifiable, but that hunting both non-game and game birds and mammals for specimens is at least equally justifiable. The state and federal warden system should be revised so that the collector and the sportsman shall be treated on the same basis. That is all I am pleading for. The laws and those officers whose duty it is to interpret and enforce them should *allow* collecting and regulate it, just as is done in the case of hunting. Those in high official position should recognize the claims of the private collector as well as the claims of the sportsman. We are responsible one to another for looking after each other's interests. Those at the top should have a care for the privileges of their minority constituency, wherever such privileges be not in serious conflict with the interests of the majority.

A further instance of inconsistency is to be noted in the intemperance with which the reservation idea has been put into effect within the last few years. The whole scheme of game refuges, and the reservation of restricted areas for safe breeding grounds for birds, is a splendid one. Its adoption on a large scale is a thing worthy of the deepest satisfaction on the part of naturalists, economists and sentimentalists alike. But hasn't it gone beyond all reason when the Aleutian chain of islands is closed absolutely to the collector; when St. Lazaria Island, southeastern Alaska, which to my knowledge has been visited by collectors just three times in twenty years, is suddenly declared a bird reservation and the regulations so fixed as to completely bar the taking of birds or birds' eggs for bona fide scientific purposes! It seems to me vastly more reasonable, economically, to put colonies of sea-birds under warden control, and at the same time to give the warden power of *allowing* moderate collecting and to see that such levy on the population is kept within the rate of productivity of the colony. It is exactly the same proposition as the gathering of mature timber from the forest reserve, or the shooting of moose and deer within certain safe numbers annually in Maine. A sea-bird colony, such as that on the Farallone Islands, would not suffer in the least if certain numbers of birds or eggs were gathered each year, totaling perhaps hundreds, just so these numbers were within the annual rate of increase. Such a course is absolutely the opposite of unlimited destruction, such as that waged by the plume-hunter. The latter violates the principles of conservation, which all men of science join with vigor in upholding.

Reasonable attention to several other factors, well known to collecting ornithologists, would far more than compensate for the toll taken by collectors. For instance, on the Farallone Islands the colonies of gulls are on the increase; the murres and cormorants are on the decrease, in spite of total protection, because of the piracy of the gulls. Many of the other birds on those islands would profit to a far greater degree if a considerable proportion of the gull population were eliminated. And this could be done easily through appropriate efforts on the part of a game warden at the beginning of the nesting season.

Collectors themselves probably fully compensate for the number of birds they destroy for specimens, in the incidental destruction by them of vermin. Collectors are practically the only people who can and do distinguish between the destructive and harmless hawks. The average collector can and does on all occasions destroy Cooper and Sharp-shinned Hawks, and in this way certainly makes up several times over for the small birds he shoots. Suggestive estimates could here be given as to the annual destruction wrought among both game and non-game birds by the few injurious species of hawks and owls. The predaceous blue-jays also receive the collector's attention.

It is true that collectors in the past have in some instances behaved indifferently toward people who are sensitive to bird killing. This lack of sympathy on the part of the collector may be one factor that has brought him into disrepute. It is to be deplored. To control the thoughtless among collectors it is feasible to devise and enforce regulations, such as one to establish say a three-mile limit around all cities and even villages of a given minimum size. By similar action already taken in some states hunting is prohibited within specified distances of "public grounds." A system of local refuges and parks, where shooting for any purpose whatever would be prohibited, would certainly be approved by most collectors and would go far toward meeting the wishes of other lovers of living birds.

It should not be forgotten that the collecting ornithologist has furnished the bulk of the reliable data upon which our game laws are based, and upon which the economic value of our non-game birds has been established. Furthermore, the training involved in bird collecting can surely be given some credit in several cases of eminent men of science who are now valuable contributors to science in other fields. The making of natural-history collections is useful as a developmental factor, even if dropped after a few of the earlier years in a man's career. Collecting develops scientific capacity; it combines outdoor physical exercise with an appropriate proportion of mental effort, both enlivened with the zest of a most fascinating and at the same time widely suggestive line of enquiry.

As a rule, all collecting adds sooner or later to scientific knowledge, either directly through printed contributions from the collectors themselves, or through the subsequent study of the material by others, often after it has been acquired by some public institution. The ultimate fate of practically all private collections is the college or museum. Very few bird skins, for instance, are destroyed except through fire or other catastrophe. They live on and on, sources of added knowledge and instruction.

In conclusion let me urge that I consider judicious collecting absolutely indispensable to serious ornithological research along certain important lines, namely, faunistics, systematics, migration, and food studies. There is still an enormous amount of investigation to be done along these lines. Right now progress is perceptibly retarded, because the field of ornithology is being avoided or deserted by the younger students. This desertion is often due to difficulties in the way of securing permits and to lack of encouragement on the part of older men. The legal attitude toward collecting should be revised so as to take in the needs and proper demands of the collector, as well as those of the sportsman.

Field Tests of Theories Concerning Distributional Control

THE CONDITIONS of animal distribution and the causes of these conditions are facts which concern intimately the problems of the persistence and of the evolution of species. The present writer believes that the field naturalist is in a position to contribute in large measure toward the solution of these problems, and it is the purpose of this paper to show how comparative studies in the distribution of species may throw light not only upon the nature of the environmental complex, but also on the relative importance of its various component factors.

Some simple facts of distribution which are of common observation, and which were early recorded by the systematic zoologist, are: (1) that each animal occupies a definite area, that is, has a habitat or range, which is distinctive enough to be included among the characters of the species and described along with its habits and the features of its bodily structure; (2) that some species (and even some of the higher systematic groups) range widely, and cover great extents of country, while others are extremely local or restricted in their distribution; and (3) that, notwithstanding considerable variation in this degree of distributional restriction, many species (or higher groups) are found nearly or entirely to coincide in range, so that sets of species, of varying ranks, may be recognized distributionally, as constituting realms, zones, faunas, subfaunas, associations, etc.

Perhaps the most prominent delimiting factor, and the one which has been emphasized through repetition in the early systematic writings, is the obvious one of physical barriers—represented by bodies of water in the case of the terrestrial species and by land in that of the aquatic. The majority of animals inhabiting islands and seas are specialized in such a manner as to be hemmed in by the limits of their respective habitats. Individuals overstepping the barrier in either case are subject to prompt destruction. This obvious type of distributional control has always been and will remain an important one for consideration; but with the acquisition of detailed knowledge regarding the distribution of animals on large continental areas, naturalists have been led to propose many other factors which have seemed to them to prevent the random and unrestricted spreading of animals over the surface of the land. The following is a list of the factors which various writers have nominated as affecting the distribution of the higher vertebrate animals. This list is complete only to the extent that my own examination of the literature is so. Many of the items have been found in dissertations upon bird migrations, which is, of course, but one phase of the general subject of distribution.

Vegetation.
Food supply, kind and quantity.
Rainfall.
Humidity of the air (relative or absolute).
Wetness or dryness of the soil.
Barometric pressure, or altitude.
Atmospheric density.
Safety of breeding places.
Availability of temporary refuges.
Water (to land species).
Land (to aquatic species).
Nature and availability of cover, or shelter from enemies.
Nature of the ground (coarse or fine soil, or rock).
Insolation, or light intensity.
Cloudiness.
Temperature: in general; mean annual; of winter; of period of reproduction; of hottest part of year.
Interspecific pressure, or competition, or race antagonism.
Parasitism.
Individual, or racial, preferences.

It is at once plain that some of the items enumerated are extremely complex, and that the most superficial analysis will show some duplication among them. For example, the factor of vegetation as influencing the distribution of different mammals resolves itself principally into the elements of food-supply and shelter, and, subordinately in most cases, into those of temperature, humidity, and nature of the soil. As some of the suggested factors may really never function in any vital degree as supposed, the total number of really critical factors is probably smaller than the total of the items just listed. Time could not here be taken to discuss the intrinsic nature of each elemental factor, even if the writer were equipped to handle such a variety of subjects; for such a discussion would in most instances lead directly into physics and chemistry, and into a study of the physiological processes of the animals affected by each of these factors. I should, however, like to dispose at once of one of the "factors" listed, and which I hear and see repeatedly cited as a cause of restriction in distribution—particularly in that of birds.

Many people claim to see in the facts of distribution only the operation of a *preference* on the part of each animal—by virtue of which, if a heterogeneous lot of animals were introduced into an area presenting diverse conditions, each species would *choose* its "natural" surroundings and rapidly allocate itself in a normal way. I grant that such a choice would almost certainly be made. In fact the hypothesis is being proved continually all over the country in connection with the migration of birds. Scores of species travel north in the spring to countries for a preceding interval unoccupied; and while, roughly speaking, they travel together, and arrive together, they segregate themselves, immediately on their arrival, and repair to separate sorts of ground, each species by itself: the pipits to the prairie, the water-thrushes to the streamside thicket, the black-poll warblers to the spruce forest, and so on. We have here an obvious choice exercised in the selection of habitats. But does this segregation of species by exercise of "individual preference" in a uniform direction change the nature of the problem in any fundamental way? Should we not here recognize merely a character in the cerebral equipment of each race, which, like every external peculiarity in its structure, is in considerable measure the result of protracted impress upon the organism from the environmental complex of factors to which the race has been subject through past time? There is no other additional factor than those environmental ones (plus the intrinsic fixedness of the species, within certain limits of plasticity, and the "evolutionary momentum") to be called into account.

As to the mechanism of geographic limitation, the adjustments to the various critical factors are inevitably forever in process, though reduced to a minimum at times of slow environmental change. The refined method of individual "preference" or "choice" is superior to the wasteful process of wholesale destruction which would be experienced by individuals finding themselves out of place as the result of a haphazard selection of locality. The frontier individuals, those on the margin of the habitat of the species, may not prosper as greatly, or reproduce as prolifically, as those in the metropolis of their species; but they certainly do not, as a rule, beat themselves to death individually against their limiting barrier, of whatever nature it may be.

To resume the main topic of this discussion, I shall attempt to show that it is possible from field observation to indicate in the case of certain species, some, at least, of the factors which control their distribution; and further that we who live in California have splendid opportunities to gather and examine data by means of which the general laws of animal distribution can be determined. An area within comparatively easy reach presents a wide diversity in topographic and climatic features. Occupying this area is an abundant complement of the higher vertebrate classes. Within the political limits of the state, systematists now recognize the presence of 388 species of mammals, 543 of birds, 79 of reptiles and 37 of amphibians. We have plenty of material to work with. I shall proceed to discuss a few selected species about which we seem to have knowledge enough to warrant provisional inferences.

THE CASE OF THE OREGON JAY

The Oregon jay (*Perisoreus obscurus*), a close relative of the Canada jay, or whisky-jack, occurs in California only in the northern third of the state. Even there it is very local in its occurrence and absolutely non-migratory. On the Warner Mountains, Modoc County, it ranges from the highest parts down to 7,000 feet altitude. On Mount Shasta it ranges from near timberline down to about 6,000 feet altitude. It is absent for a long distance to the west, through the Trinity mountain mass, but it recurs along the seacoast of Humboldt County, within fifteen miles of the ocean. And here is the curious point: along this coast strip it does not range higher than 300 or 400 feet above sea level, although there are mountains not far inland which rise to an altitude of several thousand feet. Let us look into this case for the purpose of determining the factors responsible for this interrupted range.

The Oregon jay, like most members of the crow family, is not restricted in diet. It eats a great variety of both vegetable and animal substances; its food varies in character according to season and local conditions. The supply of any particular kind of food is not likely, therefore, to be a controlling factor in its distribution.

The bird is a forest dweller. Its equipment as regards manner of flight and course to take in case of attack by enemies is adjusted to a forest habitat, and nowhere within the writer's knowledge does this jay extend its range beyond the limits of woods of some sort. Although somewhat predaceous itself, it has regular enemies among hawks and owls, for protection from which it makes use of forest vegetation. This factor of forest cover, then, must be counted as essential. But the range of the bird is not continuous wherever forests extend.

In the interior of California it does not descend below a certain altitude. Now three other factors in its distribution are quite obviously connected with that of altitude, namely, barometric pressure, atmospheric density, and temperature. But when we take into account the fact that the Oregon jay exists at or close to sea level around Humboldt Bay, the first two factors, those of pressure, and air density, are instantly eliminated, because of the obvious fact that the bird successfully maintains itself in localities of widely differing altitude where these factors are thus extremely diverse.

With reference to temperature, we know without recourse to instrumentation that there is a decrease upwards at an average rate of 3 to 4 degrees F. per thousand feet. If, then, the bird is limited downwards at a critical point, the inference apparently follows that temperature is the determining factor, and this conclusion is inevitable if we consider only Mount Shasta and the Warner Mountains. But the bird's occurrence at Humboldt Bay complicates the problem. In order to reconcile these facts of distribution we must look into the situation with reference to season. On doing so we discover that the home of the Shasta and Warner jays is subject to severe winters with heavy snow, very much colder than the winters at Humboldt Bay, where the climate is equable and snow rarely falls. But the summer temperature at Humboldt Bay is well known to be much cooler than that of even somewhat higher regions in the interior, up to an altitude of at least 4,000 or 5,000 feet, because of the eastward moving air-currents, which are coolest where they first leave the sea surface and warm up as they pass farther and farther inland. We are therefore led directly to the final inference that the summer temperature at sea level about Humboldt Bay closely approximates the summer temperature at from 6,000 to 9,000 feet on Mount Shasta and above 7,000 feet on the Warner Mountains. In these three areas, the air is cooler in summer than in the interlying areas and thus better adapted to the finely adjusted requirements of the Oregon jay. *Summer* temperature, between certain degrees, is one critical factor.

Three more factors present themselves for consideration in

connection with the Oregon jay, those of humidity, rainfall and cloudiness. Humboldt Bay lies in the most humid and continuously rainy section of California. Mount Shasta and the Warner Mountains are relatively arid, the latter most notably so. It would appear, therefore, that humidity, rainfall and cloudiness had little or nothing to do with cutting off the range of this bird, though one or other of these factors may have been responsible for the very slightly darker tone of color which distinguishes the coast jays (subspecies *Perisoreus obscurus obscurus*) from those in the interior (*P. o. griseus*). But, however this may be, it is clear that temperature must dominate greatly over the three factors named in checking dissemination.

In summary, we may therefore dispose of the following factors as having little or no effect on the distribution of the Oregon jay as a species: the nature or quantity of its food supply, atmospheric density and pressure, cloudiness, rainfall, humidity of the air or soil, and winter temperature. This eliminates all but the two factors: shelter of a sort provided by the forest habitat, and temperature of the summer season.

The Case of the Cony

The cony or pika is a mammal represented in California by four quite similar races (*Ochotona taylori, O. schisticeps schisticeps, O. s. muiri,* and *O. s. albatus*), which agree distributionally in occupying a very restricted habitat along high mountain crests. I know of no place in central California where conies range below an altitude of about 8,000 feet, and they range upwards to fully 12,000 feet in the vicinity of Mount Lyell. They thus occupy an altitudinal belt between extremes 4,000 feet apart. With regard to zones of vegetation conies live from considerably below timberline to considerably above timberline. Extended observation shows that their existence is in no way correlated with that of trees or shrubs of any sort. Like their relatives, the rabbits, they feed entirely on low vegetation, biennials mostly; but unlike most kinds of rabbits they are strictly dependent for safety from enemies upon rocks, especially where these are loosely piled as in talus slopes and so afford deep retreats within their interstices. The whole equipment of a rabbit is clearly adapted to foraging in the open, its keen hearing and eyesight quickly warning it of the approach of enemies, and giving it time to escape by means of its unusual running powers. But the cony is equipped in a very different way, as it has relatively small ears and eyes, and small hind legs. It is compelled to forage close to or beneath cover. In fact in field observations it is rarely seen on the move except momentarily, and then only between or beneath angular granite blocks, where it grazes on such little patches of vegetation as are within immediate reach.

It it clear from numerous observations that the cony is sharply restricted in a large part of its range by the rock-pile habitat. Even at favorable altitudes it is not found away from this refuge. There are obviously, however, one or more additional factors in its distribution. In many parts of the Sierras, talus slopes occur from near the highest summits down to the foothills. As examples of these, one may cite the vast earthquake taluses of the Yosemite Valley proper, which occur almost continuously down to and below the 4,000-foot contour. These taluses have been searched diligently both by trapping and hunting, without our naturalists finding a trace of conies below 8,000 feet. The animals are easy to detect, by reason of their characteristic cry, uttered at any time during the day, though more particularly in the morning and the evening, and by the accumulations of their feces, the pellets constituting which are, in size, shape and texture, unlike those of any other mammal. What is it, then, that limits the conies downward on the western flank of the Sierras, where their necessary rock habitat is continuous, and where food of the right sort is also continuous? Let us try barometric pressure, and atmospheric density, which may properly be considered together. These conditions change sensibly with altitude and, if we take into account California alone, the facts would seem to entitle them to serious consideration as active delimitors of the conies downward. But as we trace the range of the conies far to the northward we are led to a different conclusion. The altitudinal limits of their range is found to descend quite regularly towards the north, until, in the case of one race, even sea level is reached, at Bering Sea. Clearly, conies, generically, are thus proven not to be affected by atmospheric pressure, or by atmospheric density, at least in as far as it is modified by altitudes up to 12,000 feet. The same fact—depression of range towards the north— discloses a third concomitant of altitude, which is also a concomitant of latitude, namely, temperature, and this is beyond doubt the determining factor. As the isotherms dip toward sea level to the northward so does the range of the genus *Ochotona*. We have, therefore, by study of geographical distribution in this case established two important controlling factors, namely (1) safety refuges of a sort provided by talus slopes and glacial moraines; (2) temperature, at least downward below the degree, correlated in the mountains of California by a mean annual or summer computation or for a briefer period at the time of reproduction, with an altitude of eight to twelve thousand feet, according to latitude, slope exposure and air currents.

It is not possible for one to say from the data in hand what the direct controlling factors of the upward limits of the cony's range may be. Taluses extend up to the highest peaks, but there is no growth of grass above about the 12,000-foot contour even on the most favorable slopes. As the disappearance of the cony in the higher altitudes is coincident with the disappearance of its food, it appears as if failure of food alone were the delimitor here; but we have no way of showing that even if food did continue the cony would be restricted upward, as it certainly is downward, by a change in temperature beyond some critical point. The cause of its delimitation downward, however, remains clear.

THE CASE OF THE ROSY FINCH

In the case of the bird called generically *Leucosticte*, or rosy finch, we find a condition astonishingly similar to that of the cony. In fact almost the entire preceding account could be made relevant here, by merely substituting the term rosy finch for cony. The ranges, altitudinal and geographical, of the two animals are almost identical. The only obvious differences appear in their ecologic relations, and consist in the lesser dependence of the bird upon shelter and in the dissimilar nature of its food. The rosy finch forages gregariously on the open slopes, near timberline and above, though its nest is hidden away in the clefts of rock ledges and taluses. It shuns the trees and bushes even where it ranges well below timberline. It feeds winter and summer upon seeds of dwarfed vegetation, including those of grass and herbs of various sorts. As far as I can see, its food and feeding habits are identical with those of such other fringillids as goldfinches and siskins. Yet the leucosticte, by the same tests as were used with the cony, is beyond any contention limited downward by an increase of temperature. We find the bird to possess various adaptive features in common with certain arctic finches, such as tufts of bristle-like feathers over the nostrils to prevent fine snow from entering. These enable the bird to spend the long winter on the cold wind-swept ridges, but at the same time would hardly prevent the bird's dropping to warmer climes if the heat were not a strongly deterrent factor.

Cases of coincidence, as instanced by that of the cony and leucosticte, among animals of widely different powers of locomotion and ecologic position, are the rule, not the exception, and impel the observer to belief in the efficacy of the controlling factor above mentioned.

THE CASE OF THE REDWOOD CHIPMUNK

The redwood chipmunk (*Eutamias townsendi ochrogenys*) is an animal confined to a very narrow but exceedingly long distributional area extending south from the Oregon line as far as Freestone, Sonoma County. Throughout this belt it is conspicuously numerous, and is usually the only species of chipmunk present, so that the limits of its range have been easy to mark definitely along the several lines explored. This rodent,

SIERRA NEVADA ROSY FINCH

by various geographic tests similar to those I have recounted for other birds and mammals, is clearly delimited away from the coast at the bounds of the well-known fog-belt to which the redwood tree and numerous other plants as well as animals belong. The chipmunk, however, depends in no way upon the redwood or any other one plant species as far as I can see, but feeds upon a great variety of seeds and fruits, like many of its congeners elsewhere.

That temperature is also a delimiting factor is shown in parts of the range of the redwood chipmunk. But atmospheric humidity or cloudiness or rainfall, factors which I have in this case failed to dissociate, together constitute or include the chief controls.

THE CASE OF THE BELTED KINGFISHER

It is to be observed that specialization for getting a particular kind of food invariably brings with it restriction of range to the territory providing that kind of food. The northwestern belted kingfisher (*Ceryle alcyon caurina*) is a good example of this. In California we find this bird present at various times of the year both along the seacoast and along various fish-supporting streams, from the Colorado River to the Klamath River and up the mountain streams to at least as high an altitude as Yosemite Valley. The kingfisher is seen during migration in many places away from streams, but it tarries at such times only where its natural diet can be procured, as, on occasion, at fish ponds in city parks. There is a unique instance of a kingfisher observed on the desert catching lizards, but exceptional occurrences of this kind are of course not to be given consideration in making generalizations.

It is observable further in regard to this species of kingfisher, that it must have earth banks in which to excavate its breeding tunnels. Lack of these along any stream, otherwise favorable, prevents the bird from staying there through the season of reproduction. Furthermore, there is also obvious temperature restriction; for, given a fish-producing stream, with banks apparently well suited for excavation of nesting places, such as is the Colorado River and its distributaries, and the summer temperature must be at least below that of southern California south of the 35th parallel. That all such streams are well supplied with kingfishers in winter, and are forsaken only during the hot summer, seems to show that a relatively cool temperature is for them in some way or another essential to successful reproduction.

We find, then, in the case of the belted kingfisher, that the factors of a requisite kind of food, and a requisite kind of nesting place, both having to do with the structural powers and limitations of the bird, together with the factor of the temperature of the summer season, are those that account for the distribution of the species within the state of California, as we find it.

THE CASE OF THE MEADOWLARK

The western meadowlark (*Sturnella neglecta*) is a bird of relatively omnivorous diet. Note that I say relatively, for the word omnivorous unmodified would apply only to such an animal as would eat the sort of food that any animal eats, and this is an obvious impossibility for the meadowlark when we consider such uncommon articles of diet as wood and petroleum. Compared with many other birds, the meadowlark does use as food a very wide range of plant and animal objects. This food, however, is restricted to a particular habitat source, namely to the meadow. The bird's entire equipment specializes it for successful food-getting and for escape from enemies upon a grassy plain or meadow. And it is a matter of common observation that its range is sharply delimited in most directions at the margin of the meadow habitat, as where this is interrupted by forest, brushland, marsh, rock surface, or sand flat. This is a conspicuous example of what we may call associational restriction. But it is not the only way in which the meadowlark is hemmed in. In this connection California again provides critical distributional evidence.

We find meadowlarks occupying practically every appropriate meadow, large and small, from the Mexican line to the Oregon line and from the shores of the Pacific to the Nevada line, *except* above a certain level on the higher mountains. In traveling up the west flank of the Sierras, and this I have now verified along three sections, meadowlarks cease to be observed at approximately the 4,500-foot level, and this in spite of the fact that above that altitude meadows are found which are to all appearances ideal for meadowlark requirements. I need only refer to such seemingly perfect summer habitats as Monache Meadows and Tuolumne Meadows. And though, in the winter these would be uninhabitable, so are other meadows (as those in the Modoc region, for instance), which are in summer warm and at that season abundantly inhabited by meadowlarks. By the elimination then upon proper grounds of various factors from the list, we have left only three possible factors in this upward delimitation, namely, decreased atmospheric pressure, decreased air density and decreased temperature of the summer season. Since meadowlarks exist at corresponding altitudes in the warmer though elevated Great Basin region, and since it has been possible to eliminate positively and in a similar way the first two factors in the cases of many other birds and mammals, these factors are presumably without influence on the meadowlark; and there is left but one—temperature.

Within the state of California, meadowlarks, without the slightest detectable subspecific modification, thrive under both the cloudy, humid conditions of the northwest coast belt and under the relatively cloudless, arid conditions of Owens Valley. Factors of humidity, of air and soil, cloudiness, and light intensity, seem to avail nothing in checking their spread. With such a degree of associational specialization as is exhibited by these birds there is little chance of a serious competitive struggle with other vertebrates, and no evidence of such has been observed. As far as California is concerned, the meadowlark's range is thus only limited associationally and zonally, that is by the extent of its particular meadow habitat and by diminished summer temperature below some critical point.

The meadowlark well illustrates some further facts with regard to distribution. In California it is unquestionably on the increase as regards total population. This is due chiefly to the great extension of habitable territory resulting from man's occupancy and cultivation of the land, bare plains, brushlands and even woods being replaced by irrigated alfalfa and grain fields. These the meadowlarks find suitable and invade because of their expansive reproductivity, and soon populate to the fullest extent permitted by the minimum annual food supply. In other words, associational barriers have moved, to the advantage of this particular bird, though at the same time to the disadvantage of endemic species of different predilections. I should estimate that the total meadowlark population in the San Joaquin-Sacramento basin is now fully three times what it was thirty years ago.

Animal distribution is not fixed. It changes with the shifting of the various sorts of barriers, and doubtless also as a result of a gradual acquisition by the animals themselves of the power to overstep barriers, as by becoming inured to greater or lesser degree of temperature. The power of such accommodation, or inherent plasticity, evidently varies greatly among different animals; and at best its operation is very slow. Many species have proved stubborn and have been exterminated, as the factor-lines, or barriers, shifted. By the shifting of, say, two critical factor-lines towards one another, the existence of a species may have been cut off as by a pair of shears.

SUMMARY

In this paper I have enumerated various factors thought to be concerned with the control of the distribution of vertebrate animals. A number of birds and mammals have been cited to show how we may use our more or less detailed knowledge of their ranges so as to demonstrate the operation of one or several out of the many possible factors as limiters to distribution. The method employed is one of examination, comparison and elimination, applied to all parts of the margin of animals' ranges.

The range of any one animal must be examined at all points of its periphery in order that all of the factors concerned may be detected. One factor may constitute the barrier in one section of the periphery of the range of a species, a totally different factor in another section.

The results of the geometric ratio of reproduction would bring about areas of occupancy in the shape of perfect circles. But we never find such symmetrical ranges. The very fact that the outlines of the ranges of animals are extremely irregular is significant of the critical nature or inexorableness of the factors which delimit them. These factors have to do with the evolution, persistence and extermination of species.

Note that we always have to take into account, in attempting to discern factors of limitation, the animal's own inherent structural equipment. This prescribes restriction at once in certain regards. Referring again to our list of suggested factors, we find the long-emphasized ones of land to aquatic species and bodies of water to terrestrial species really presenting an extreme manifestation of associational restriction. Food source, methods of food-getting and safety refuges are involved.

It is to be noted further that the factors are various and that the most important factor for one species may prove of little effect with another species. Species do not react uniformly to the same environment. It is undoubtedly always a combination of factors which accounts for an animal's geographic range in all parts of the periphery of that range. It is most certainly never one factor alone. No one will claim that temperature is the *only* delimiting agent in controlling vertebrate distribution; nor could this claim be made for humidity alone, or for food supply alone, or for safety of breeding-places alone.

Given a large continuous area, however, as upon the North American continent, one single factor does happen to loom up as being the most frequent delimiter of distribution, or even the ultimately effective one, in greater or less degree, even though other factors be effective also. This factor is temperature. The cases cited illustrate the tenet that in some direction or another, temperature beyond certain limits, up or down, cuts off further dissemination. This is part of the basis of the life-zone idea. But, as I have tried to bring out above, this fact is in no way antagonistic to the claim that other factors, as of humidity, food supply, and shelter, also figure critically, giving a basis for recognizing faunal areas and associations. Finally, if our discussion of the subject has been sound, it is evident that data secured through field observation can be so employed as to bring results essentially similar to, and as conclusive as, those secured through laboratory experimentation.

The English Sparrow Has Arrived in Death Valley: An Experiment in Nature

THE ENGLISH SPARROW first became well established in the United States in 1860–1864 in the vicinity of New York City. Several small plants had been made in other Atlantic cities within the few years preceding, but practically all of these are definitely known to have failed. The original stock is in nearly all the cases of importation known to have been obtained in England. Its spread through the eastern United States after once established was phenomenal; its rate of invasion towards the west only slowed up at about the 100th meridian, and this, significantly enough, is about at the line limiting a great many species of native eastern birds toward the west and of native western birds toward the east. Nevertheless, the English sparrow ultimately crossed this barrier, constituted by change in humidity, and it has continued expanding its range until it exists now in nearly every part of every state in the Union. It has also extended throughout southern Canada and has become well settled in the Hawaiian Islands.

In California the English sparrow was first noticed in 1871 or 1872, in San Francisco, and it quickly thereafter appeared in many of the towns in the west-central part of the state. But it was very slow to enter southern California. It did not reach Los Angeles for nearly thirty-five years, in 1907; and San Diego was not reached until 1913. To-day it is familiar in practically every town "south of Tehachapi." Among the places in California now inhabited by the English sparrow, to designate some of those showing extremes of climate as regards temperature and humidity, are Brawley, Imperial County, and Sisson, Siskiyou County; Needles, San Bernardino County, and Eureka, Humboldt County.

In 1917 the California Museum of Vertebrate Zoology undertook as field work for that year a study of the vertebrate animal life of the Inyo region of southeastern California. In connection with this work it was the writer's not unpleasant fortune to spend the month of April in Death Valley. What was his surprise to find there a thriving colony of English sparrows. These were established on the Greenland Ranch (otherwise known as Furnace Creek Ranch), elevation 178 feet *below* sea level. Specimens were collected, both as alcoholics and as dry study skins, but not to an extent to threaten the persistence of the colony. For here, it occurred to the writer, we had at hand a particularly convincing "experiment" already under way, of just the sort called for by certain critics of the work of the systematist and distributionist, which in time would test the question of the evanescence versus the relative permanence of characters of the category commonly viewed as subspecific.

The sparrows of Furnace Creek Ranch, which were estimated to number about fifty, had their main headquarters in the tops of the several tall Washington Palms which overshadow the ranch house; also several nests were seen in the Fremont cottonwoods which line the irrigation ditches along the alfalfa fields for a quarter of a mile down toward the glistening borax flats. The traveller on entering Death Valley is impressed by Greenland Ranch as a wonderfully rich oasis surrounded by a desert of surpassing barrenness. The English sparrow colony there is, then, isolated under a climate that is probably of the greatest extreme in the direction of high temperature combined with low relative humidity, of any place in North America.

Greenland Ranch is owned by the Pacific Coast Borax Company, who value it for its output of alfalfa hay and for certain appurtenant water rights, there being a constant flow of forty inches from the warm springs nearby. Fortunately for our present problem, the company has for years required its managers to keep a daily record of weather conditions. There is a standard instrument shelter, and the records are kept in available form, and furthermore have been transmitted regularly to the

United States Weather Bureau. Without going into details here, it is of interest to note that the highest recorded temperature for any place in the United States was observed there on July 10, 1913, when an afternoon temperature of 134° Fahrenheit in the shade was reached.

As to the time of appearance of the sparrows in Death Valley I have good reason to rely on the statements of Mr. Oscar Denton, who is the present manager of the Greenland Ranch. He says that he first saw them in the ranch yard five years ago (1914). That was about the time the Death Valley spur of the Tonopah and Tidewater Railroad was run to the present location of Ryan. Ryan, by the way, is the terminus of the narrow-gauge line, wherever that terminus happens to be, and this shifts about as determined by the extent of the different ledges of borax ore mined. The borax deposits on the floor of Death Valley are no longer gathered. The day of the 20-mule-team borax wagons is gone except on the labels. It is cheaper to handle the richer borax ore high on the mountain sides and to reach these ledges by railroad. The present Ryan, the nearest the railroad has so far gotten to Death Valley, is 17 miles from Greenland Ranch and 3,000 feet altitudinally above it. I saw English sparrows there repeatedly in April and May, 1917, as also at Death Valley Junction, 40 miles farther away, on the Tonopah and Tidewater Railway. Mr. Denton believes, and I think he is likely right, that the sparrows followed the construction camps along the route of the T. & T. R.R. from Ludlow to Death Valley Junction and thence along the narrow-gauge to Ryan. It may be further suggested that since hauling is done from time to time down the 17 miles of Furnace Creek Wash from Ryan to Greenland Ranch this is the route probably traveled by those sparrows which reached Death Valley. It is less probable to my mind that the birds simply started out overland, from some more distant point, and a pair or more just happened to reach this remote and forbidding valley. It is true, however, that the green of the ranch shines out conspicuously for miles around about and would surely attract to it any vagrant sparrow coming within sight.

We here in America have been accustomed to think of the English sparrow as a full *species, Passer domesticus*. The bird was originally named by Linnaeus, and thus has seemed from all standpoints to constitute a truly "Linnaean species." However, recent developments in the geographic knowledge of birds in the Old World has brought out the fact of geographic variation within the species *Passer domesticus* as previously understood, and also that a number of forms once considered specifically distinct are really connected with the *domesticus* stock through ordinary geographic intergradation. Hartert (1910, pp. 147–151) after a study of the group came to recognize no less than eight subspecies occupying different areas in Europe, western Asia and northern Africa. Subsequently, at least two more races have been named. And now, a German, Kleinschmidt, has discovered that the sparrows of England are distinguishable from those on the continent. The latter, having been the basis of Linnaeus's name, becomes *Passer domesticus domesticus,* and the sparrow of England Kleinschmidt names (cited under date 1915, though I have not seen the original description myself) *Passer domesticus hostilis.* As pointed out by Oberholser (1917, p. 329), since the American stock came from England our bird must also be known under this name. And furthermore, the vernacular term, European house sparrow, which some people have preferred because of a fancied unpleasant association in the name English sparrow, can not be used properly for the American bird.

The point I wish to make now is that the English sparrow, which is spread all over the United States, is itself a subspecies of a wide ranging and decidedly variable species which is thus, geographically speaking, quite like our American song sparrow, or the horned lark. In the Old World, each race "stays put" as regards aggregate of population, each in its own faunal area just as do our own song sparrows. All of these races are non-migratory. *Passer domesticus hostilis* Kleinschmidt is also non-migratory, as far as I have been able to learn, wherever it now occurs, north and south, in America. But here, by reason of its marvellous powers of accommodation, and finding no competitor in exactly its own ecologic niche, it has gradually advanced its frontiers and overleaped all the faunal boundaries which hem in the habitats of our native bird races; and we find flourishing representations of it under the most diverse conditions of environment, as for example those shown in contrast by Death Valley and Boston.

Possibly our critics have been merely baiting us when they asked us to transplant a desert song sparrow to the humid coast belt and "see what would happen." But is not this demand met exactly in the case of the English sparrow, only in reverse direction? I have carefully compared the seven skins taken in Death Valley with others taken in Berkeley, and also with examples taken in the eastern United States, without finding any peculiarities of color tone, extent of markings, or dimensions. And I think my eyes are pretty well trained to find small subspecific distinctions, at least of such magnitude as characterize the currently recognized subspecies of song sparrows, Savannah sparrows, and horned larks. The Death Valley birds, it is true, stand out rather sharply from most of the material taken elsewhere, but only in that they are fresh and clean, and lack the sooty overcast of the majority of town birds. To repeat, no differences are now discernible from place to place in North America, in so far as perfectly comparable material is at hand. This accords with the findings of Phillips (1915), which also were practically negative.

Are we not to infer, then, that there has not as yet been sufficient time (up to three years and as many possible generations in Death Valley and up to sixty years elsewhere in North America) for the impress of diverse environments in the different parts of the territory newly occupied by *Passer domesticus hostilis* to bring physical changes in the birds of sufficient magnitude for the modern systematist to detect? Is there not here a demonstration of the relative permanence of subspecific characters far beyond what many naturalists have supposed? Are not such characters in general far more likely to be germinal than somatic?

How intensely interesting it will be to watch the course of this "experiment," now under way, irrespective of human effort, in Death Valley, with "controls" vigorously maintaining themselves (against man's wish!) in San Diego, Berkeley and Boston.

But perhaps it will be urged that the conditions of an orthodox experiment are not here properly met. The "factors" of the environment are not sorted out, and none is under any kind of regulation. Moreover, rigid control has not been secured, in that there is no way in which any of the naturally established colonies of English sparrows can be strictly isolated and kept from genetic contamination by new influxes of birds from elsewhere.

In reply, I would say that we are not expecting more from our natural experiment than the demonstration of what we set out to prove, namely, the length of time necessary for the development, in a stock under natural conditions some of which are known, of characters of subspecific value. In the breeding cage there are always "unknown" factors; so let us admit the existence of those in the wild as not invalidating the "experiment" as such. In nature, subspecies *have* differentiated under just the conditions self-imposed by the English sparrows through their powers of invasion. *Individual* song sparrows and horned larks are continually overstepping the bounds of the habitats of the races to which they belong and have doubtless done so since the initiation of their respective descent lines. But differentiation of the mass *has taken place, under just these conditions.*

Sequestration Notes

THERE is every reason to believe that the voices of birds have been subject to a process of evolution which has led from the simplest beginnings to a condition which is rather complicated in the higher present-day species. The first sounds uttered by primitive birds were doubtless entirely of an incidental nature, due to expulsion of air under stress of pain or fear, or simply of physical impact. According to one theory (Witchell, 'The Evolution of Bird-Song', London, 1896) the first specialization accompanied combat and involved a meaning of defiance or intimidation; from this it was an easy step to notes conveying the idea of alarm to other individuals of the same species.

Whatever the course in the early development of bird voices, it is obvious to any field student that in the higher existing birds an often very elaborate system of cries or calls obtains, with an associated wide range of meaning; as witness the Titmouses and Ruby-crowned Kinglets. Some of the meanings, in certain species, have been demonstrated beyond all question of doubt. The less obvious meanings will have to be worked out by slow process, and exceeding care be taken to avoid mere guess-work.

A seemingly adequate method of deciding upon the meaning of bird voices is to note as accurately as possible (1) the exact nature of the sounds produced in all particulars, and at the same time (2) the behavior of the bird when uttering each kind of note, and (3) the conditions obtaining with respect to all extraneous factors such as relate to activities of other individual birds in the vicinity, other animals, cover, and forage. The degree of reliance upon the inferences from such observations will increase with the number of times these observations are repeated. The final and satisfactory explanation will not be forthcoming at once, though it is well to hold whatever meaning presents itself even from the outset as a tentative hypothesis.

Some years ago the attention of the present writer became directed to the behavior and notes of certain non-flocking passerine birds as exhibited during the winter season. Dearth of other ornithological features of interest at that season was probably the circumstance which favored the development of the following ideas. The particular class of notes here to be considered are those of the category commonly called "location" or simply "call" notes, and are uttered at irregular intervals by certain birds when foraging singly under normal conditions.

To be more explicit, the birds in the writer's experience especially concerned are the Ruby-crowned Kinglet (*Regulus calendula*) and Audubon's Warbler (*Dendroica auduboni*). The common winter call-note of the former is the familiar rachety, tone-less noise, of three or more sections or syllables. The usual call-note of the latter is the rather sharp single syllable, *tsip*. The notable thing with both species is that their notes are uttered at rather frequent intervals, though irregular ones, by each individual as it forages *alone*. There are often to be heard in the distance, many trees away perhaps, other individuals of the same species; but a point of importance here is the essentially non-flocking habit in both the species under consideration.

I am aware that Ruby-crowned Kinglets do occasionally assemble to a limited extent in winter; for example when "mobbing" an owl. Or, late in the afternoon, as many as five or six individuals may be found in the same tree on a sunny upper hill-slope, especially if the trees be scattering. Also, Audubon's Warblers sometimes collect in numbers up to a dozen or more in one tree, such as a blossoming eucalyptus, or in a clump of fruiting *Rhus laurina*. But the individuals in all such gatherings show themselves to be thoroughly independent of one another; each goes his own way; and there is, indeed, frequent evidence of friction or conflict of individual interests. There is no indication of coördination of movement, as with truly flocking birds: no individual advantage is gained by the gathering.

Observation of any one Ruby-crowned Kinglet under the

usual winter-day conditions in southern or west-central California, shows it to be almost continually intent upon its search for insects. Its mode of search, and the category of insects which its equipment fits it to make use of, direct its forage course as a rule through thick leafy terminal foliage of evergreen trees and shrubs, less generally, perhaps, among the stems of willows and alders, where, however, there are usually left-over, curled-up leaves, and plenty of crannies behind buds and in clefts of forking twigs, to harbor small insects. But insects are relatively scarce in winter, increasingly so as the season advances; and the Kinglet's scrutiny must be rapid. Each individual Kinglet *must cover much territory in limited time* in order to gather the food in sufficient quantity.

As it thus forages, each Kinglet every now and then utters its note, or series of notes. Another individual, or others, may be heard from time to time in the distance, but I have failed altogether to receive the impression that two or more birds "answer one another." My experience is that they most certainly do *not* come *towards* one another as the result of such calls. And here the idea presents itself, logically, that these notes serve to keep the foraging birds *apart:* they are *sequestration notes.*

The nature of the conditions which call forth this category of notes, which makes them of *use* in the struggle for existence on the part of the species, would seem to me to be as follows. The Kinglet is a foliage forager and is most of the time within or in close reach of adequate cover; hence for the most part it is safe from both aerial and terrestrial predators. It relies for food upon small insects, mainly stationary, which in the winter season are not abundant, sometimes exceedingly scarce, as shown by occasional periods when some of the birds starve; the Kinglet cannot dig after its insects or uncover them, but must look for them in plain sight; it must scrutinize a large area of leaf and twig to find enough, and it must *avoid duplicating territory that its neighbor Kinglet has scrutinized.* In other words it is of critical need that the individuals of a species whose food is of this nature, and must be gotten in this way, be continually *spaced out* over the available food producing territory. Two or more individuals must not follow each other's paths or look over the same ground, at least until there has been time for insect life to move about again.

With Audubon's Warbler the conditions are very much the same as with the Ruby-crowned Kinglet, save that the forage beat of the former lies, as a rule, in more open trees and bushes, or on the outer surfaces of masses of foliage. The *tsip*-notes are uttered seemingly for the same general purpose, to keep neighboring individuals from duplicating territory. With both the Warblers and the Kinglets, it is not uncommon in winter to see two individuals, which may happen to encounter one another in the same tree, assume a hostile manner of behavior and tone of voice. The latter consists in each case, of the same sort of expression as the sequestration note, but uttered with more emphasis. In the case of male Kinglets, there are flashes from the unfurled coronal, and one of the birds quickly puts the other to flight; each is soon pursuing separate forage routes in different directions.

In the case of the Audubon's Warblers, again, it is quite true that two or more individuals often enter into loose membership in the roving aggregations of birds which travel about the open country in winter and include in their number, bluebirds, certain sparrows and even pipits. And also one often encounters a number of Audubon's Warblers, not in company of other birds, trailing along in the same general direction, with indications that they are trying to keep in loose contact with one another. And here it is possible a shade of meaning in their voices invites collectivity. Indeed one can conceive of a note being both centrifugal and centripetal in meaning, the latter to a given radius, the former beyond. But now our discussion has departed into the realm of speculation.

In thus assigning the function of sequestration to certain notes of certain birds, the writer has placed confidence in an accumulation of impressions received during a number of years of observation. The species concerned are among our

commonest everyday winter birds. Verification of this explanation, or the refutation of it, should be easy to secure on the part
of persons who are interested in the natural history of living
birds; for there are many such nowadays, in excellent position
to make accurate observations, and to make from these valid
inductions.

The Principle of Rapid Peering, in Birds

OBSERVATION shows that the commoner birds may be divided into two categories with regard to their method of obtaining food. The two categories comprise, first, those kinds of birds which perch and wait passively for the appearance, within reach, of moving objects of food value; and, second, those birds which themselves are almost continually in motion and thereby seek out items of food which are stationary. It is not to be inferred that all birds will fall definitely into one or the other of the classes here described. Indeed, some species will come to mind which occupy a borderland position; and furthermore, there are other types of behavior altogether, as illustrated by the vultures and by the owls.

As an instance of the first category, let us recall the behavior of a Hermit Thrush (*Hylocichla guttata*). The bird moves along the shaded ground for a distance, then strikes a statuesque pose during which it surveys with intent eye the ground round about. If nothing attracts its attention, the bird shifts its field of vision ahead, by another advance of a few feet, and again assumes a rigid pose. Occasionally the field of possibilities is improved by the bird's flicking over with its bill a leaf or two. But always the statuesque pose is quickly resumed. If, during this pose, some object on the ground happens to move, it catches the bird's eye, by reason of this movement, and is captured.

Another example of this first category is afforded by the Black Phoebe (*Sayornis nigricans*), which selects an open perch three or four feet above the ground where it sits until some insect flies by. Then the bird, having quickly sighted the insect by reason of the latter's motion, sallies forth and, with remarkable accuracy of aim, snaps it up.

In these two birds, and in scores of others which will come

to mind, such as the Great Blue Heron and the White-rumped Shrike, the relation is that of a *motionless* predator on the lookout for *moving* prey.

The second category is well illustrated by the Brewer Blackbird (*Euphagus cyanocephalus*) when it forages on a lawn. The bird walks rapidly and continuously, turning this way and that, with head moving quickly to and fro in unison with its footfalls. The motion of the head involves changes in the position of the eyes; and the bird is able, with wonderful acuteness, to detect among the grass blades motionless insect larvae. A gullet-full of these larvae, to be conveyed to the waiting young blackbirds, is obtained in an amazingly brief period.

It is this second type of behavior that I wish to discuss in an endeavor to arrive, if possible, at an acceptable explanation. The more I reflect upon the observed actions of birds, and of animals generally, the more I am confirmed in the conviction that there is no such thing as wasted effort. In other words, the "excess-of-vigor" idea, or more poetically the "joy-of-living" concept, does not properly explain the lively, sprightly, cheerful, joyous aspect of many birds—although these humanistic terms are often applied to them, even in our more serious ornithological literature. Really, every movement, every phase of activity, has its explicit meaning in the bird's program of maintaining existence. Hence an adequate explanation of these movements, involving stern utility, should be looked for with earnestness by every serious naturalist.

Let us now cite the commonly observed actions of the Ruby-crowned Kinglet (*Regulus calendula*). People sometimes term this bird vivacious or nervous, because of its rapid or seemingly fidgety movements. Elliott Coues designated it as "the picture of restless, puny energy, making much ado about nothing." As a person watches the Kinglet passing through and over the peripheral foliage of a tree, incessant motion is, to be sure, its striking feature. This motion is seen to involve both the whole body, as operated by wings and clinging feet alternately, and the head, a member to be looked upon as the vehicle not only of the beak, the instrument of capture, but of the eyes, the chief sense organs concerned with the search for food. Even when poised out in front of a spray of foliage, on rapidly beating wings in almost the manner of a hummingbird, the Kinglet is continually moving his head this way and that. By virtue of this incessant motion on the part of the eye, he sees in relief, as he could not otherwise, the outlines of the motionless, fixed scale insect, the aphid, or the leaf caterpillar, and thereupon apprehends such insect, to devour it if it prove of food value.

Thus, the Brewer Blackbird, the Ruby-crowned Kinglet, most of the Warblers, and numerous other birds in the same behavior category, seek after *stationary* objects, and locate them by means of *rapid movements* on their own part. Our own human experience will help here in making the explanation clear.

Of easy verification is the greater ease with which a person catches sight of a distant moving object as compared with the same or a similar object at rest. Any hunter will recall the experience of having nearly or quite passed an object (such as a deer or a rabbit), in plain sight all the while, without noticing it—until the moment it moved; then as it started up and traveled across the background in which all other objects were stationary, the eye was quickly attracted to it and held by it.

The result of the reverse situation is, it seems to me, similar. That is to say, when one is looking for an object, such as a golf ball in the grass or an animal which he knows to be stationary like everything else in the background of bushes or trees, then he, the searcher himself, moves back and forth, at the same time intently observing the objects at varying distance from him as the seemingly differential movements separate them from one another so that perspective is emphasized. Indeed it is instinctive for a person to crane his neck, as the saying goes, to move the head and the upper part of the body this way and that, when looking for an object in the near distance. Objects all of the same color, shape, and size, or nearly so, which are at different distances will be separated out of the background, when viewed by an eye in side to side motion, as they never could be separated if viewed by an eye in a fixed position. The principle of the parallax, in astronomy, obviously enters here, in that an apparent displacement of the object observed is brought about by the actual displacement of the observer.

Furthermore, rate of movement bears direct ratio to ease of detection; the more rapidly an object moves across the landscape, the quicker is it picked up by the eye—within certain practical limits. The slow movements of a snake or a land salamander are much more likely to be overlooked than the sudden dash of a rabbit or a mouse. And conversely, the faster a searcher moves, again within certain limits, the quicker will he "pick up" the object sought.

To refer to the birds again, think of an individual of an insectivorous species, one closely fitted by structure into an ecologic niche so that its food is restricted in kind and location but must be found in adequate quantity to meet the needs of a high-pressure organism. Such a bird must cover much territory every day in order to get this requisite food supply. Remember that the maintained bodily temperature of passerine birds varies from 107 to 111 degrees F., and that their rate of living must be so much faster than our own as to make very difficult, on our part, an understanding of the sensations and reactions of such birds to their surroundings. Their experiences in an hour may total our own experiences of a day.

To get food is relatively easy for the Kinglets and Warblers when insect life is plentiful, in spring and summer; the remittal of the exigencies of food-getting then allows for the carrying on of other essential functions, such as reproduction and molting. But sooner or later there comes a time of lessening food supply, more or less of an annual famine period. And this is *the* critical time in the existence of the individual and also of the species. It is during these recurrent periods of most extreme food shortage that the whole equipment of the bird, including such intangible things as phases of behavior, is put to the vital test. The merest twist of the head may then be a matter of life and death. There is then no chance for parleying with stern nature. Recall the enormous expectation of casualty in, say, Kinglets—approximately 300 per cent annually, figured on the basis of the minimum population at the advent of the breeding season. In other words, 300 must perish each year for the 100 that survive until May.

All these considerations lead me to look for, in the forage behavior of different birds, specializations which adapt each bird closely to its own food source. One class of food items is characterized by motility and is chosen by a category of birds with particular structures and behavior coördinated with what might be called a phlegmatic temperament. Another class of food items is characterized by fixity—lack of motion. To obtain this class of food the bird called nervous or vivacious applies *the principle of rapid peering*. This faculty of rapid peering enables it to find successfully small stationary objects in foliage and among branches or grass blades, *as if these objects were moving and the bird itself were quiet.*

The Museum Conscience

THE SCIENTIFIC MUSEUM, the kind of museum with which my remarks here have chiefly to do, is a storehouse of facts, arranged accessibly and supported by the written records and labeled specimens to which they pertain. The purpose of a scientific museum is realized whenever some group of its contained facts is drawn upon for studies leading to publication. The investment of human energy in the formation and maintenance of a research museum is justified only in proportion to the amount of real knowledge which is derived from its materials and given to the world.

All this may seem to be innocuous platitude—but it is genuine gospel, never-the-less, worth pondering from time to time by each and every museum administrator. It serves now as a background for my further comments.

For worthy investigation based upon museum materials it is absolutely essential that such materials have been handled with careful regard for accuracy and order. To secure accuracy and order must, then, once the mere safe preservation of the collections of which he is in charge have been attended to, be the immediate aim of the curator.

Order is the key both to the accessibility of materials and to the appreciation of such facts and inferences as these materials afford. An arrangement according to some definite plan of grouping has to do with whole collections, with categories of specimens within each collection, with specimens within each general category, with the card indexes, and even with the placement of the data on the label attached to each specimen. Simplicity and clearness are fundamental to any scheme of arrangement adopted. Nothing can be more disheartening to a research student, except absolute chaos, than a complicated "system," in the invidious sense of the word, carried out to the absurd limits recommended by some so-called "efficiency expert." However, error in this direction is rare compared with the opposite extreme, namely, little or no order at all.

To secure a really practicable scheme of arrangement takes the best thought and much experimentation on the part of the keenest museum curator. Once he has selected or devised his scheme, his work is not *done*, moreover, until this scheme is in operation throughout all the materials in his charge. Any fact, specimen, or record left out of order is lost. It had, perhaps, better not exist, for it is taking space somewhere; and space is the chief cost initially and currently in any museum.

The second essential in the care of scientific materials is *accuracy*. Every item on the label of each specimen, every item of the general record in the accession catalog, must be precise as to fact. Many errors in published literature, now practically impossible to "head off," are traceable to mistakes on labels. Label-writing having to do with scientific materials is not a chore to be handed over casually to a "25-cent-an-hour" girl, or even to the ordinary clerk. To do this essential work correctly requires an exceptional genius plus training. The important habit of reading every item back to copy is a thing that has to be acquired through diligent attention to this very point. By no means *any* person that happens to be around is capable of doing such work with reliable results.

Now it happens that there is scarcely an institution in the country bearing the name museum, even though its main purpose be the quite distinct function of exhibition and popular education, that does not lay more or less claim to housing "scientific collections." Yet such a claim is false, *unless* an adequate effort has been expended both to label accurately and to arrange systematically all of the collections housed. Only when this has been done can the collections be called *in truth scientific*.

My appeal is, then, to every museum director and to every curator responsible for the proper use as well as the safe preservation of natural history specimens. Many species of vertebrate animals are disappearing; some are gone already. All that the investigator of the future will have, to indicate the nature of such then extinct species, will be the remains of these species preserved more or less faithfully, along with the data accompanying them, in the museums of the country.

I have definite grounds for presenting this appeal at this time and in this place. My visits to the various larger museums have left me with the unpleasant and very distinct conviction that a large portion of the vertebrate collections in this country, perhaps 90 per cent of them, are in far from satisfactory condition with respect to the matters here emphasized. It is admittedly somewhat difficult for the older museums to modify systems of installation adopted at an early period. But this is no valid argument against necessary modification, which should begin at once with all the means available—the need for which should, indeed, be emphasized above the making of new collections or the undertaking of new expeditions. The older materials are immensely valuable historically, often irreplaceable. Scientific interests at large demand special attention to these materials.

The urgent need, right now, in every museum, is for that special type of curator who has ingrained within him the instinct to devise and put into operation the best arrangement of his materials—who will be alert to see and to hunt out errors and instantly make corrections—who has the *museum conscience.*

The Role of the "Accidental"

THE TOTAL NUMBER of species and subspecies of birds recorded upon definite basis from California amounts at the present moment to 576. Examination of the status of each species, and classification of the whole list according to frequency of observation, show that in 32 cases out of the 576 there is but one occurrence known. In 10 cases the presence of the species has been ascertained twice, in 6 cases three times, and for all the rest there are 4 or more records of occurrence. Some 500 species can be called regularly migrant or resident.

Examination of the records for the past 35 years shows that the proportion of one-occurrence cases is continually increasing. In other words, the state is so well known ornithologically that regular migrants and residents have all or nearly all of them been discovered, and *their* number now remains practically constant, while more and more non-regulars are coming to notice. This might be explained on the ground that there are continually more and better-trained observers on the lookout for unusual birds. This is probably correct, partially. But also, I believe, there is indicated a continual appearance, within the confines of the state, through time, of additional species of extra-limital source.

In puΓlished bird lists generally, species which have been entered upon the basis of one occurrence only, are called "accidentals." This is true of county lists, or state lists, and, quite patently, of the American Ornithologists' Union's 'Check-list of North American Birds'. The idea in the adoption of the word "accidental" seems to have been that such an occurrence is wholly fortuitous, due to some unnatural agency (unnatural as regards the behavior of the bird itself) such as a storm of extraordinary violence, and that it is not likely to be repeated. This understanding of the word "accidental" is borne out by the explicit meaning given it in the 'Century Dictionary', for instance, which is "taking place not according to the usual course of things," "happening by chance or accident, or unexpectedly." Now the way in which the word is used by ornithologists is really a misapplication of the term; for, as I propose to show, the occurrence of individual birds a greater or less distance beyond the bounds of the plentiful existence of the species to which they belong is the *regular thing, to be expected*. There is nothing really "accidental" about it; the process is part of the ordinary evolutionary program.

However, as I have intimated, the word is firmly fixed in distributional literature. We had better continue to use it; but let us do so with the understanding that it simply means that any species so designated has occurred in the locality specified on but one known occasion. No special significance need to be implied.

Accidentals are recruited mostly from those kinds of birds which are strong fliers. It is true that the majority belong to species of distinctly migratory habit. But some of our accidentals exemplify the most sedentary of species. Examples of one-instance occurrences, in other words "accidentals," are as follows: the Western Tanager in Wisconsin, the Louisiana Water-Thrush in southern California, Townsend's Solitaire in New York, the Catbird on the Farallon Islands, the Tennessee Warbler in southern California, and Wilson's Petrel on Monterey Bay. In the North American list some of the accidentals come from South America, some even from Asia and from Europe.

I would like to emphasize the point now that there is no species on the entire North American list, of some 1250 entries, that is not just as likely to appear in California sooner or later as some of those which are known to *have* occurred. Expressing it in another way, it is only a matter of time theoretically until the list of California birds will be identical with that for North America as a whole. On the basis of the rate for the last 35 years, 1⅗ additions to the California list per year, this will happen in 410 years, namely in the year 2331, if the same intensity of observation now exercised be maintained. If observers become still more numerous and alert, the time will be shortened.

It will be observed that there are now many more one-occurrence, "accidental," cases than there are two-occurrence cases, and that there are more of the two-occurrence group than there are three-occurrence, and so forth, there being a regular reduction in the intervals so that, if we just had enough observations, a smooth curve would probably result. If the one-instance occurrences should continue to accumulate without any modification of the process, in the course of about 300 years there would be more of these "accidentals" in California than of regularly resident species, and the other groups would grade down in a steeper curve. I attempted to carry out the figures, which seem to behave according to some mathematical formula; but when I came to deal with three-fifths of an occurrence I decided it was profitless to go on!

It is evident, however, that another process takes place, of quite opposite effect. With the lapse of time second-occurrence cases replace one-occurrence cases, to be followed by a third order of accretion, and this by a fourth; and the process might continue on ad infinitum, until theoretically, sometime after the full number of the North American list had been reached, our state list would no longer contain any accidentals at all. To cite an example, the eastern White-throated Sparrow was recorded first from California, and then as an accidental, on December 23, 1888; in 1889 a second specimen was taken; in 1891, a third was taken, and so on until in 1921, 19 occurrences have been recorded. This species is considered now simply as rare, certainly not accidental, casual, or even specially noteworthy save from a very local standpoint.

It comes to the mind here that if observations could be carried on so comprehensively as to bring scrutiny each year of every one of the 200,000,000 birds in California, this being the estimated minimum population maintained within the state from year to year, a great many more accidentals would be detected than are now known, and in addition some birds now known from but a few records, or even as accidentals, would come to be considered of frequent, though not necessarily regular, occurrence. With the White-throated Sparrow it is not impossible that a thousand of the birds have wintered in California in certain years.

Some of the considerations in the preceding paragraphs, while of interest in themselves perhaps, have confessedly been rather beside the issue. For the definite question which I wished to ask and which I will now briefly discuss is as to the function or role played by accidentals. Are they a mere by-product of species activity or do they in themselves constitute part of a mechanism of distinct use to the species?

The rate of reproduction in all birds, as with other animals, is so great that the population rapidly tends toward serious congestion except as relieved by death of individuals from various causes or else by expansion of the area occupied. The individuals making up a given bird species and occupying a restricted habitat may be likened to the molecules of a gas in a container which are continually beating against one another and against the confining walls, with resulting pressure outwards. But there is an essential difference in the case of the bird in that the number of individual units is being augmented 50 per cent, 100 per cent, in some cases even 500 per cent, at each annual period of reproduction, with correspondingly reinforced outward pressure.

The force of impingement of the species against the barriers which operate to hem it in geographically, results in the more than normally rapid death of those individuals which find themselves under frontier conditions. There follows, through time and space both, a continual flow of the units of population from the center or centers toward the frontiers.

The common barriers which delimit bird distribution are as follows: Land to aquatic species and bodies or streams of water to terrestrial species, the climatic barriers of temperature, up or down beyond the limits to which the species may be accustomed, and of atmospheric humidity beyond critical limits of percentage; the limits of occurrence of food as regards amount and kind with respect to the inherent food-getting and food-using equipment of the species concerned; and the limits of occurrence of breeding places and safety refuges of a kind prescribed by the structural characters of the species requiring them.

An enormous death rate results from the process of trial and error where individuals are exposed wholesale to adverse conditions. This can be no less, on an average, than the annual rate of increase, if we grant that populations are, on an average, maintaining their numbers from year to year in statu quo. But before the individuals within the metropolis of a species succumb directly or indirectly to the results of severe competition, or those at the periphery succumb to the extreme vicissitudes of unfavorable conditions of climate, food or whatnot obtaining there, the latter have served the species invaluably in *testing out* the adjoining areas for possibly new territory to occupy. These *pioneers* are of exceeding importance to the species in that they are continually being centrifuged off on scouting expeditions (to mix the metaphor), to seek new country which may prove fit for occupancy. The vast majority of such individuals, 99 out of every hundred perhaps, are foredoomed to early destruction without any opportunity of breeding. Some few individuals may get back to the metropolis of the species. In the relatively rare case two birds comprising a pair, of greater hardihood, possibly, than the average, will find themselves a little beyond the confines of the metropolis of the species, where they will rear a brood successfully and thus establish a new outpost. Or, having gone farther yet, such a pair may even stumble upon a combination of conditions in a new locality the same as in its parent metropolis, and there start a new detached colony of the species.

It is this rare instance of success that goes to justify the prodigal expenditure of individuals by the species. Such instances, repeated, result in the gradual extension of habitat limits on the part especially of species in which the frontier populations are in some degree adaptable—in which they can acquire modifications which make them fit for still farther peripheral invasion against forbidding conditions.

Incidentally, the great majority of these pioneers are, I believe, birds-of-the-year, in the first full vigor of maturity; such birds are innately prone to wander; and furthermore it is the autumnal season when the movement is most in evidence, a period of food-lessening when competitive pressure is being brought to bear upon the congested populations within their normal habitats. The impetus to go forth is derived from several sources.

The "accidentals" are the exceptional individuals that go farthest away from the metropolis of the species; they do not belong to the ordinary mob that surges against the barrier, but are among those individuals that cross through or over the barrier, by reason of extraordinary complement of energy, in part by reason of hardihood with respect to the particular factors comprising the barrier, and in part of course, sometimes, through merely fortuitous circumstances of a favoring sort.

Geologists tell us that barriers of climate are continually moving about over the earth's surface, due to uplift and depression, changes in atmospheric currents, and a variety of other causes. Animal populations are by them being herded about, as it were, though that is too weak a word. The encroaching barrier on the one side impinges against the population on that side; the strain may be relieved on the opposite side, *if* the barrier on that side undergoes parallel shifting, with the result that the species as a whole may, through time, flow in a set direction. If anything should happen that a barrier on one side impinged on a species without corresponding retreat of the barrier on the other side, the habitat of the species would be reduced like the space between the jaws of a pair of pliers, and finally disappear: the species would be extinct.

But, in the case of persistence, it is the rule for the population, by means of those individuals and descent lines on the periphery of the metropolis of the species, to keep up with the receding barrier and not only that but to press the advance. I might picture the behavior of the population of a given bird as like the behavior of an active amoeba. This classic animal advances by means of outpushings here and there in reaction to the environment or along lines of least resistance. The whole mass advances as well. The particles of protoplasm comprising the amoeba may be likened to the individuals comprising the entire population of the animal in question, the mass of the amoeba to the aggregate of the population.

It is obvious that the interests of the individual are sacrificed in the interests of the species. The species will not succeed in maintaining itself except by virtue of the continual activity of pioneers, the function of which is to seek out new places for establishment. Only by the service of the scouts is the army as a whole able to advance or to prevent itself being engulfed: in the vernacular, crowded off the map—its career ended.

The same general ideas that I have set forth with regard to birds, who happen to be endowed with means of easy locomotion, hold, I believe, also for mammals, and probably in greater or less degree for most other animals. I can conceive of a snail in the role of an "accidental," an individual which has wandered a few feet or a few rods beyond the usual confines of the habitat of its species. Given the element of time (and geologists are granting this element in greater and greater measure of late), the same processes will hold for the slower moving creatures as they seem to do for those gifted with extreme mobility.

Migration, by the way, looks to me to be just a phase of distribution, wherein more or less regular seasonal shifting of populations takes place in response to precisely the same factors as hem in the ranges of sedentary species.

The continual wide dissemination of so-called accidentals, has, then, provided the mechanism by which each species as a whole spreads, or by which it travels from place to place when this is necessitated by shifting barriers. They constitute sort of sensitive tentacles, by which the species keeps aware of the possibilities of areal expansion. In a world of changing conditions it is necessary that close touch be maintained between a species and its geographical limits, else it will be cut off directly from persistence, or a rival species, an associational analogue, will get there first, and the same fate overtake it through unsuccessful competition—supplantation.

The Trend of Avian Populations in California

THERE IS ONE besetting temptation to which any student fairly advanced in the exploration of his chosen field would seem justified in yielding. This temptation is to hold up to close scrutiny any striking generalization given wide publicity, save it be from the most authoritative source—to see whether it be really founded in fact. A case in point has to do with avian populations.

It has been stated or at least implied with increasing frequency in late years, in various publications, especially in those emanating from organizations concerned with bird protection, that serious decrease is taking place in our bird life, and that this decrease is due to the thoughtlessness or perfidy of man and is preventable. These statements and implications are being expressed not only with regard to the longer and more thickly settled eastern United States, but with regard to the west in general, and to California. Confessedly with some *a priori* doubt, but with a view to testing fairly the truth of these dicta, I have undertaken an inquiry into the situation in our own state, for the purpose of finding out what the facts are—of ascertaining whatever changes in our bird population may, indeed, have become apparent, and the causes therefor.

To begin with, of course, terms must be defined. In using the word "decrease," or its opposite, "increase," in this connection, one of two distinct ideas may be in a person's mind. He may refer to the *number of species*, or he may refer to the aggregate *number of individuals*. Or, both of these ideas may be held, in more or less vague association.

To take up the first concept: There is no question whatsoever that a certain few species of birds have become nearly, or quite, extinct, as far as California is concerned, within the past seventy-five years; as examples, the trumpeter swan and the whooping crane. But, compensating for these losses, there have become newly established within our territory during that same period some species of foreign source; as examples, ring-necked pheasant and English sparrow. Checking up the species of both categories, we can reach but the one conclusion that, as yet, so far as concerns the state as a whole, there has been no real reduction in the total number of species; our known avifauna at the present moment totals 582 species and subspecies; I am aware of no good ground for supposing that it was one unit more or less, seventy-five years ago.

If, however, we narrow our attention to given restricted localities, we are confronted with evidence of real and great reduction in species, up to even forty per cent. of the original number, I figure, in some places. It is this *local* reduction in species, most apparent naturally in centers of human population, that has impressed so strongly the ardent advocates of the various sorts of bird protective measures.

An entirely different phenomenon, as already intimated, is comprised in the fluctuation of aggregate populations, irrespective of the various species, few or many, represented in them. On this point, my impressions are strong that, throughout the country at large, wherever human influence has had any marked effect, there has been *increase* in the bird life. In some localities, as pointed out below, this increase may reach as much as tenfold.

My reader will at once demand something more tangible than "impressions." And I am compelled regretfully to admit that actual figures seem to be wanting. We have no record of censuses taken fifty years ago, or even twenty-five years ago. This is unfortunate; and it is to be hoped that further lapse of time will see an improvement in this situation. Numerical censuses, on either an areal basis or a unit-of-time basis, are now being taken and recorded. The student of the future, let us hope, will have plenty of statistical data upon which to base final conclusions.

It seems, then, that, in this discussion, I must fall back upon

less tangible classes of evidence—upon memory and upon inferences from other categories of facts. Before citing this evidence,
however, let me introduce some theoretical considerations.

It is a recognized, established principle that the presence in
a region of any given bird species is absolutely dependent upon,
first, proper food supply, second, the right kind of breeding
places, and third, appropriate cover or protection for individuals—each of these conditions as bound up with the inherent
structural features of the bird under consideration. Mark that
there are *three* of these factors, each and all of them essential;
if any one of them in a given region becomes effaced, the bird in
question can no longer exist there. There are, of course, other
factors essential to avian existence, but they affect all the birds
of a given fauna alike. We can deplore, wring our hands, and
suffer agonies of regret, but to no avail—except as active steps
be taken to restore the critical condition. As a matter of cold
circumstance, a bird's disappearance in a given locality may be
irretrievable—as happens where man has densely settled a territory and incidentally or purposely destroyed certain of its
natural features unnecessary or inimical to his own existence
there. Chop down all the trees and there can be no more woodpeckers; drain the lakes, ponds and swamps and there can be
no more water birds; remove the chaparral, and wren-tits,
bush-tits and thrashers can no longer find proper food and
shelter. Cement up all the holes in the campus oaks and there
will be no more plain titmouses—for the reason that roosting
and brooding places essential to their existence are no longer
to be found.

Each bird species native in a given region has a different and
very special combination of requirements. Existence of each
is really determined by a very slender thread of circumstances
which can, in most species, be broken readily. Differences
must, of course, be recognized in the degree of hardihood, or
of viability, in the various species of birds—some are on the
ragged edge of extinction, this condition in part due to inherent reduction in specific vigor—the race is naturally playing

out, we say; others are hardy, with a large reserve of specific energy; some can even stand what may aptly be called ecologic punishment.

In any one locality the field observer comes to recognize a few or many rather intangible units which he calls "ecological niches"—separate cubby-holes or dwelling places or habitats (in the narrowest sense), which differ in essential respects from one another. If the topography and vegetation be varied, there are many of these niches; if more uniform, there are few of them. Each niche is separately occupied by a particular kind of bird, and the locality supports just as many species of birds as there are niches; furthermore, the numbers of individuals of each bird are correlated directly with the degree of prevalence or dominance of the niche to which that particular bird is adapted. In other words,—and here is the crux of the idea,—both the number of the species and the number of the individuals of each species, in a locality, are directly dependent upon the resources of the environment, from an avian standpoint. The same notion holds, of course, for all other animals, including *Homo*.

Rate of reproduction in any species has been established down through past time so as to supply the population needed to keep the appropriate niche filled. This rate varies with the natural prevalence of the niche, and with the hazards to which the niche occupant is exposed. Not only that, but a wide margin above the normal need is provided to meet that extreme emergency which may arise but once in a thousand generations; in other words, there is produced a large surplus—an apparent great waste—of individuals over and above what is needed to keep the appropriate territory fully populated, in order to save the species from extinction at some critical moment; for animate nature abhors a vacuum no less than does inanimate nature. A recent writer in SCIENCE (LV, May 12, 1922, pp. 497–505), Professor A. F. Shull, has, in another connection, called this fact of over-production the "factor of safety." He says: "The entire struggle for existence is based on the principle that security and advancement are best assured through wasteful over-production." The employment of the factor of safety, I would say, is a manifest device on the part of nature to insure continuity of species, and hence also to make evolution possible.

A British ornithologist, Mr. H. E. Howard, has lately put out a book in which he elaborates exhaustively the idea of the importance of territory to bird life. Kind and availability of territory determine the kind and amount of bird life. In final analysis, when a territory, or, as I would express it, more explicitly, an ecological niche, becomes *full,* and this in normal times comes to pass very quickly, the individuals within the species constitute each other's worst enemies. Continued conflict for space—for a piece of land, for an area of meadow, for a section of tree-trunk, for a given unit of volume of twiggery or foliage—is plain to be seen by any diligent observer of bird life. The resulting pressure for territorial expansion reminds one of the same pressure obtaining among humans; only, among birds, there is no organized warfare. The process is one of struggle as between individuals or pairs of individuals, between neighbors, indirectly, perhaps, as a rule; but also, often, directly, by personal action. The most fit to compete, sometimes the most fortunate, will survive; the less fit will be eliminated. The survival prospects of each single individual are small. Vast numbers of individuals are poured in. The "safety factor" in numbers is there in order to insure the persistence, and continued adaptive improvement, *of the species.*

Let us now return to more matter-of-fact considerations. What have been some of the effects of the settlement of California by the white man, upon the environments of birds? Have any ecological niches been effaced? Have any niches been added? Have some been reduced in prevalence and others increased in prevalence, relatively? What have been the effects upon the niche-occupants?

Perhaps the most conspicuous changes wrought in the appearance of the landscape in the southwest have resulted from irrigation. In substantiation of this statement, many of my readers can doubtless appeal to his own memory. I, myself, recall traversing long stretches of the San Joaquin Valley twenty-five years ago, which were then merely arid plains. The vegetation consisted of xerophilous grasses and herbs, with here and there tracts of lupine or atriplex bushes. The birds observed were scattering horned larks, fewer meadowlarks, and occasional burrowing owls; it being winter, there were more numerous Savannah sparrows and, in rain-dampened places, pipits. Knowing what I do now about censuses, I doubt if there were then more than one bird to an acre, on the average, probably much less than that ratio.

Now, regarding the same territory, it would be hard to exaggerate the amount of change in vegetation which has resulted from the watering of the ground. Orchards, alfalfa fields, green pastures and streams of running water lined with willows, completely occupy the land. Instead of a very uniform type of environment, with only a few niches and correspondingly few species of birds, one finds, upon analysis, a great variety of niches and a much increased number of bird species. What is more, the numbers of *individuals* are vastly larger. To be sure, the horned larks and burrowing owls are gone. But the meadowlarks have multiplied; and, in addition, one sees great numbers of Brewer blackbirds, of mockingbirds, goldfinches, swallows, phœbes and killdeers. I estimate the mean population over large areas of the San Joaquin in April, when the lowest ebb for the year is reached, at 10 per acre, or over 6,000 per square mile. Here, obviously, the conditions for abundant avian population have been markedly improved by the coming of the white man with his methods of cultivation.

Even more spectacular has been the faunal change wrought by irrigation in Imperial Valley, where luxuriant vegetation with resulting abundance of bird life has replaced the original sparse vegetation of the desert which supported relatively little animal life.

Another biotic modification is brought about by deforestation. Close stands of coniferous trees are replaced by "slashes," by open young growths, or by mixed brush land and trees. Dense forests, it is well known, are sadly lacking in bird population. The removal of the forests has meant, of course, the disappearance of a few, specialized avian tenants. But in their place, occupying the clearings and mixed growths, is a much greater population both as to individuals and species. Kinglets, pileated woodpeckers, and hermit thrushes may have disappeared; but fox sparrows, chipping sparrows, spotted towhees and a host of other birds of like habitat preferences have come in. Certain little niches have been done away with; but the change in the nature of the territory at the hand of the lumberman has resulted in there being many more, new niches; each of these, evidently, of greater amplitude, of greater supporting power.

Very definite change in the other direction has been that made as a result of the draining of swamp lands. Many species thereby have been eliminated, locally, many more species than occupy the reclaimed land; and, furthermore, I feel sure that the numbers of individuals, too, have been reduced, though not in so large proportion. As instances, I would refer to Nigger Slough and Gospel Swamp in southern California, and to the region at the confluence of the Sacramento and San Joaquin Rivers in west-central California. A swamp is really a very complicated type of environment; within it usually may be recognized *many* "niches" and a correspondingly large number of avian occupants. Among these are the herons, rails, gallinules, song sparrows, yellow-throats and tule wrens and, if there be open water, coots, terns and several species of ducks.

The most serious adverse effect of the human occupancy of California upon bird-life thus far has, I believe, resulted from this reclamation of the swamp lands. But, if you will resort to memory, or examine a topographic map, you will observe that the total area here involved is very small compared with the territory that has been affected oppositely, by irrigation. Irrigated territory, moreover, is subject to continual and much farther spread, while the possibilities of drainage are almost exhausted.

Other modifications of primitive conditions as a result of the white man's occupation of the country are as follows: By the clearing of brushlands, for example, in San Fernando Valley, Los Angeles County; by the planting of trees, afforestation, as exemplified in the groves of trees around the Greek Theater and on the Berkeley hills; by the cultivation of dry grasslands, as on the coastal benches of San Diego County; and by the formation of storage reservoirs and canals, which, irrespective of the lands which they water, bring into existence aquatic and riparian types of vegetation conducive to an abundant bird life. Some of these it will be noted, check against one another, so that *status quo,* in part of the country, tends in some measure to be maintained.

In general, then, my contention is that there has been, on the average, as a result of the settlement of California, a marked increase in our bird population. Bird life at large has benefited—and this in spite of various adverse features which also have been imposed. My message should be, therefore, one of optimism to the bird-lover. It is to be understood that I refer to birds of all groups together; not to any particular group. There are vastly more of the so-called "song birds," numerically, than there are of the "game birds" and "birds-of-prey." The latter two groups have been seriously depleted, unquestionably, from various causes associated with man; but probably not more than ten per cent. of our original bird population consisted of game birds and birds-of-prey combined.

Permit me now to link up with current notions and beliefs in regard to the status of bird life some of the ideas that I have been endeavoring to express. In a large proportion of cases the reduction or disappearance of a cherished species of bird, locally, such as may have been laid to other entirely different causes, has really been due simply and inevitably to the reduction or complete effacement of the kind of habitat the bird must have for its existence; in other words, its ecologic niche has been reduced in volume, or destroyed. No one could help it; nor can any one now stay the process, except by restituting the lost factor; for example, when land is bought or otherwise preserved from human use and devoted to the use of the birds, as in national or state bird or game reserves. Of course, in certain areas, such as national parks and forest reserves, the environments and the birds occupying them are being preserved anyway, incidental to other interests.

The tendency among sentimentalists has usually been to seek out a cause for the disappearance of birds that is directly concerned with their fellow men. The hunter, the boy with the sling shot, the collector, any one of them or all, loom up as *the* "exterminators of birds"; whereas, in truth, I believe, it is only in rare cases and then only very locally, that *these* agencies have had any effect at all. In other words, if my line of reasoning has been correct, legal protection, with ninety per cent. of our bird species, is absolutely unnecessary, save as it applies, and then properly so, to parks, the suburbs of cities, and to logically constituted game and wild-life preserves, where shooting for *any* purpose is out of order.

Recall the geometrical ratio of reproduction, and the consequent powerful potentiality for recovery on the part of bird species. Let me cite here the case of the eastern bluebird as reviewed by Mr. P. A. Taverner in a recent number of the *Canadian Field-Naturalist* (XXXVI, April, 1922, pp. 71–72). In the winter of 1895–96 a cold wave swept the South Atlantic states, the sole wintering ground of the eastern bluebird. As a result, famine and death reduced the total bluebird population almost, but not quite, to the vanishing point. But in five years the species had recovered "from almost nothing to practical normality." After reaching normal, a "saturation point of population" for the species, it ceased to increase; or, as I would express it, its ecologic niche, of fixed amplitude, was then full. The operation of the "factor of safety" not only saved, but very quickly brought back, the species.

Another catastrophe, recorded by Dr. T. S. Roberts (*Auk*, XXIV, 1907, pp. 369–377) happened to a sparrow-like species, the Lapland longspur, in southwestern Minnesota, the middle of March, 1904. It was migration time, and a peculiarly wet and thick snowstorm that occurred during the night of the thirteenth is thought to have overwhelmed the birds when in flight high overhead, soaking their plumage and dazing them. At any rate, great numbers hit the ground with fatal violence. In the morning dead and injured birds were to be seen over a wide stretch of country; on the frozen surfaces of two lakes 750,000 dead longspurs were counted, by the method of laying off sample units of area and checking the birds to be seen on these units. But in spite of this spectacular destruction of individuals the Lapland longspur was not reported the following years in the winter range of the species (Kansas, etc.) as obviously less numerous than usual. Did not the ability of the species to recover from this extraordinary calamity rest in the "factor of safety"?

There is good reason to believe that release of intra-specific pressure on the breeding grounds of a species is accompanied by greater productivity on the part of the remaining population. The survival chances for the young are greater where the safest type of nesting places is available to all the adults seeking to breed, and where congestion of population, and consequent drain on available food supply, has been relieved. Also, towards the end of the year, when the annual pinch of food scarcity comes into play, in the winter range, a larger proportion of maturing individuals than usual will survive. In other words, from one point of view, calamitous reduction of population benefits the immediately oncoming generations.

Let me center attention now upon the significant fact that certain of our birds are, and always have been, totally *un*protected by either law or sentiment—jays, crows, linnets, shrikes and blackbirds. The rate of annual increase in those species is no different, in so far as I am aware, than it is in the vireos, warblers, mockingbirds, tanagers, and purple finches, which latter are looked upon as desirable song birds. Yet the former are holding their own just as well as the latter, protected, species. Their numbers are always kept up to topnotch commensurately with the prevalence of their niches. They have reached the maximum population possible to them, consistent with the nature of the country, and they hold to it.

We all know of the enmity of orchardists, and agriculturists, and sportsmen toward linnets, blackbirds and blue jays, respectively. Now and then, and there is a case on record as far back as thirty years ago, "blue jay hunts" are held; in one lately recorded instance, at Hollister, San Benito County, 1,531 California jays were killed in one day, in a prize competition for the destruction of so-called "vermin." Incidentally, you will note that sportsmen feel particular animosity toward any competitor or rival in their own field! They are right after anything that can be called "vermin" from their standpoint. As far as we can see, as a result of such campaigns—shooting of blue jays, netting of blackbirds, and poisoning of linnets—there has been only a very temporary and local reduction in the numbers of these birds; two or three seasons bring them back to normal: that is, to the maximum numbers which the amplitude of their respective niches will warrant.

Bird population, in kind and quantity, is controlled primarily by conditions of habitat. It is a matter of food and shelter. The natural history collector, as a factor against birds, is only an exceedingly minor influence, one which like all the others, is allowed for by the "factor of safety." My readers will begin to suspect that I have become sensitive because of the inveighing that certain well-meaning but uninformed people have undertaken against the killing of birds for specimens. I admit the score.

The Burrowing Rodents
of California
as Agents in Soil Formation

THE INTERRELATIONS between vertebrate animals and their environments are exceedingly variable and far-reaching. To base any conclusion upon a contrary assumption has proven dangerous, for in specific cases such procedure has led people to expend effort and substance not only needlessly but definitely against their own best interests. An inference as to the relationships between some certain wild mammal and human affairs may at first thought look to be perfectly obvious and unquestionable. Extended examination, however, may show that many factors previously overlooked are concerned, and the comprehension of these may lead to an entirely different view.

The species and subspecies of mammals occurring in California, so far as known at the present moment, number 410; 227 of these belong to the order Rodentia. Of these, 109 are essentially burrowing rodents, that is, they have their breeding quarters at least, beneath the surface of the ground, this circumstance entailing more or less digging; and some of them spend practically all of their time within their subterranean tunnels. These rodents of essentially burrowing habit include the following groups: The ground squirrels, with 18 species; the kangaroo mice, with 2 species; the pocket mice, with 23 species; the kangaroo rats with 33 species; and the pocket gophers, with 33 species.

To express the above facts in more general terms: Of the total number of species of mammals living within the confines of the state, more than one-half are rodents, and of the rodents alone, just one-half are of the burrowing category; rodents that burrow constitute, by species, one-fourth of all the mammals in California. It may further be observed that rodents which burrow are more or less plentiful throughout the West. And here is another surprising fact, namely, that only one of the seven genera of mammals to which our burrowers belong is represented in the United States east of the Mississippi River. (The genus *Citellus* of ground squirrels furnishes the exception; two species of that genus go as far east as Indiana.) From a possibly economic bearing, with respect to digging, moles and earthworms, though ecologically not at all homologous, seem to take the place in the far eastern states that the burrowing rodents take here.

The line of demarcation, eastward of which the burrowing type of rodent begins to disappear, is, approximately, the 100th meridian. In other words, there is a north and south line of transition between two major faunal regions which roughly coincides with this meridian. The limitations of the animals in question undoubtedly have to do with the physical peculiarities of the regions east and west of the 100th meridian. These peculiarities involve differences in atmospheric humidity, in rainfall, and, of seeming major importance, the sharp alternation of dry and wet season which occurs to the westward. Linked up with these conditions, there is, probably, in the West a relatively greater abundance of plants with nutritious roots or thickened underground stems (corms, rootstocks).

With regard to abundance of mammals in California by individuals, I have made numerous estimates. It proves to be highly variable, all the way from zero per acre, as on parts of the floor of Death Valley, up to 120 per acre, as in certain parts of the San Diegan district. I have figured a conservative average throughout the entire state to be 20 mammals of all sorts per acre, so that the total mammal population in California, at the period of the year just before the breeding season, when the population is at its lowest ebb, is 2,000,000,000. Estimating further, on the basis of the results of trapping and of field observation in different parts of the state, I find that the population of *burrowing* rodents is at the very minimum one-half that of *all* the mammals, which would thus be in the aggregate about 1,000,000,000.

Even cursory observation suffices to establish to one's satisfaction the relative abundance of such burrowing types of mammals as ground squirrels, pocket gophers, and kangaroo rats. Along any of the railroads or highways, interminable stretches of the right-of-way, or of the adjacent plains or mountain slopes, show a profusion of the so-called "workings" of these animals—mounds, trails, mouths of burrows (open or closed), caved-in burrows, winter earth-cores, and the like. If a person starts out on foot, he will inevitably "fall in" to subterranean runways; every little while he steps through into some tunnel or cavern. The surface of the ground is seen to be nearly covered with disturbed soil showing footprints of these animals, especially if the season be the dry one. The vegetation will show abundant evidence of having been foraged upon by rodents.

Of the five types of burrowing rodents in California, the most widespread, in the aggregate the most abundant, and certainly the most effective in its equipment for turning over the soil, is the pocket gopher (*Thomomys*); and upon this type I propose chiefly to dwell. An examination of a pocket gopher shows its structure throughout to be remarkably specialized for burrowing into and through the ground. A study of its habits shows that in all probability a pocket gopher spends at least ninety-nine one-hundredths of its existence below ground. Its world is limited by the earthen walls of a cylinder. In one direction this cylinder brings safety from enemies; at the other end it brings accessibility to food. We find that the gopher is deficient relatively to other rodents with respect to eyesight. Its hearing is likewise below the average and seems to be keenest for sounds of very low rate of vibration, such as jarrings of the ground. Its sense of touch is localized not only in the nose and surrounding vibrissæ, but also at the tip of the tail. The animal moves quite as well backward in its burrow as forward; it needs to be apprised of conditions in both directions.

The body as a whole is short, thick through, with a notable massiveness anteriorly—just the opposite of the litheness of structure characteristic of, say, the squirrels. The head of a pocket gopher is larger in proportion to its body than is that of any other land mammal in California. The head is joined to the body without any obvious neck constriction, and the shoulders are broad. The bigness of the head is accounted for both by the thicker and more ridged bones of the skull and by the greater mass of the muscles attached to them. These are correlated with the structure, position and operation of the relatively huge incisor teeth.

The mouth is a vertical slit, guarded by furry lips which are appressed so as to keep out the earth loosened by the projecting incisor teeth or pushed ahead of the animal by means of the face and fore feet. The pocket gopher is our only mammal in which the incisor teeth can not be concealed within the lips.

Comparison of the pocket gopher, as an extreme type of digger, with the California ground squirrel, which is also a digger but to a far less degree, shows some significant differences. An average adult California ground squirrel weighs 681 grams; an average adult male pocket gopher weighs 170 grams, close to one-fourth as much. But the weight of the skull of the ground squirrel is 7.8 grams, while that of the gopher is 7.2 grams, practically the same. In other words, the skull of a gopher is four times as heavy as that of a ground squirrel, total weights considered. The brain-case, however, seems to have relatively about the same capacity in the two animals. The skull and teeth of the pocket gopher, together with the musculature connected with them, comprise the chief engine of digging. Its operation results in cutting away, and in part transporting, the earth, as the animal extends its underground system of passage-ways. But there are also supplementary digging structures. Instead of the hind feet being larger than the fore feet, as in most mammals, the reverse is the case in the pocket gopher. We find the fore feet are larger and provided with long stout curved claws; and the forearm and shoulder are heavily muscled. Through and

Illustrates extent to which the ground may be worked over and perforated by burrowing rodents (in this case, *Dipodomys* and *Perognathus*). Photo taken by J. Grinnell, May 4, 1911, near Earlimart, Tulare County, California.

A pocket gopher, *Thomomys bottae pascalis*, photographed from freshly taken specimen to show certain structural features; for instance, upper incisors projecting beyond furry orifice of mouth. Snelling, Merced County, California, May 28, 1915. Photo by C. D. Holliger.

Illustrates way in which burrowing rodents turn over the soil; a light-colored sand from below is deposited, unconformably, on top of the dark-colored surface stratum. The pocket gopher here concerned was *Thomomys perpallidus perpes*. Photo taken by J. Grinnell, June 21, 1911, near Onyx, Kern County, California.

In this case a stony substratum is brought to the surface where its rate of weathering will be hastened; in other words, the presence of burrowing rodents is accelerating the process of soil formation and this, in course of time, will mean improvement in the crop of native grasses or other plant growths. The pocket gopher responsible for this work was *Thomomys bottae minor*. Photo taken by J. Dixon, December 12, 1917, near Gualala, Mendocino County, California.

through, the adaptations of the pocket gopher are seen to be concentrated for the digging function.

I have excavated several tunnel systems of gophers and have recorded the diameters in various portions of their courses, and the volumes of the earth removed. I will not take space to give the figures here. Suffice it to say that the ordinary runs maintain a remarkably uniform diameter and depth below the surface of the ground. The depth varies from four to eight inches, depending upon the consistency of the soil—clayey and coherent, or sandy and loose. The deeper extensions of the burrows, down to a depth of 20 inches, lead to the breeding chambers where the nests are located.

As already intimated, pocket gophers appear above-ground rather seldom; they do so, as a rule, only as necessary to push out surplus earth loosened in the extension of their tunnels or to forage in the near vicinity of the open burrows. While gophers are active throughout the entire 24 hours of the day, new surface workings, marked by dark damp soil, are to be found chiefly in the morning.

The typical mound is of a fan shape, the opening of the burrow from which the earth was pushed, although closed, being clearly indicated at the base of the fan. The upraised surface of the fan is marked by more or less sharply indicated concentric "moraines," each registering the terminus of an operation from the mouth of the burrow. The rim of the mound is often irregular, the earth having been pushed farther out at some points on the periphery than at others. The mouth of the burrow is plainly outlined in a perfect circle of raised earth two to three inches in diameter, but this small circle is always lower than the preponderance of the heap.

However, a great deal of the gophers' activity at the surface of the ground is not marked by the presence of mounds. Especially during the dry season, one will find at frequent intervals circular openings in the ground which have been filled with loose earth, nearly or quite to the level of the surrounding surface. Examination will show that these burrows have been used as exits from short side branches of the main tunnels. They are used for the purpose of exploring the immediately adjacent surface for food.

A gopher is loath to leave its shelter and ordinarily does not venture as far even as the length of its body from the open mouth of its burrow. As an evident result of this timidity, each feeding exit is the center of a small circle, shorn of vegetation, the radius of which is less than the body length of the gopher. The haunches of the animal, when it forages, remain in contact with the orifice of the burrow, as a sort of anchor by means of which the gopher can pull itself back into safety at an instant's warning. It is well known to gardeners that a gopher will burrow underground to some nearby plant, rather than risk capture by venturing forth on the open surface. Many times gophers tunnel toward the surface beneath plants and cut off roots and even main stems, without any disturbance being evident above-ground, until the plants begin to wither and die, if they do not topple over before by reason of insecurity at the base.

In digging, the earth loosened by the strong incisor teeth and stout front claws is swept back underneath the body until a considerable amount has accumulated. The animal then turns around (being able to do so apparently almost within the diameter of its own body, which is the diameter also of its burrow), and pushes the earth along the tunnel to the surface opening where it is shoved out on top of the ground or into some other part of the burrow system no longer of use. Only the fore feet, in conjunction with the broad furry face below the level of the nose, are used in moving the earth. The outside-opening, fur-lined, cheek pouches, with which the animal is provided, and which are situated at each side of the mouth, are not used to carry earth, but solely to carry clean food materials. Most of the surface openings are at the ends of side tunnels and are but a few inches in length. After excavation has proceeded a few inches beyond one surface opening, this opening is closed and a new one is made at a more con-

The winter earth-plugs here shown, as left when the snow melted on the lodge-pole pine forest floors, serve to bury much vegetational débris; with subsequent decay of this organic material the humus content of the soil is increased. Such a process of bringing up soil from beneath, of consequent gradual settling of the surface, and of burial of vegetable remains, parallels quite closely in final results, on wild land, what the farmer does when he plows his cultivated acres. The pocket gopher doing the work in this particular case was *Thomomys monticola*. Photo taken by C. D. Holliger, June 19, 1915, near Mono Meadow, Yosemite National Park, California.

venient location—nearer the point where the earth is being removed.

As already intimated, gophers occur very widely. In fact, in California, we find them existing under the most extreme conditions of climate, though different *species* are represented under the different combinations of conditions. There are pocket gophers in abundance in the vicinity of Yuma, and at Eureka; at Monterey, and around Goose Lake; at Fresno, and up to the limit of plentiful plant growth, 11,500 feet, on the slopes of Mount Whitney.

I will now give some facts and information relative to the gophers in the Yosemite National Park, where Mr. Tracy Irwin Storer and myself have made definite studies of their habits.

The pocket gopher* is one of the few Sierran rodents that carry on active existence throughout the entire year. It does not hibernate, so far as we know, even at the highest altitudes. There is good evidence of the continued work of gophers there, beneath the snow, however deep this may become. During the winter and spring in the high country, where the snow lies deep, they are led to adopt a somewhat different method in extending their tunnel systems than during the summer months. The tunnels are then made in the snow itself, a greater or less distance above, and in most of their courses more or less parallel with, the surface of the ground. These snow tunnels are usually greater in diameter than the subterranean runs, perhaps because of the loose texture of the snow as compared with that of the soil beneath; they serve the purpose of allowing the gophers to reach plants which are imbedded in the snow. Many of them are used also in extending the subterranean systems. The earth from below-ground is carried up and packed in the snow tunnels previously dug, thereby forming solid earth cores above the level of the ground. When the snow melts in the spring, these cores are lowered intact onto the surface of the ground, where they often remain more or less recognizable for several months, despite the winds and summer thunder-

---

* The species here concerned is *Thomomys monticola*.

showers. The height to which the snow tunnels extend above the ground depends upon the depth of the snow-fall; but there is reason to believe that their general course is modified by the position of the above-ground vegetation encountered. After the snow has gone, in early spring, we have found portions of earth cores lying on top of flattened branches of snow-bush, on fallen tree branches, on logs and rocks, indicating that the animals had pursued courses in the snow well above these objects. When active right after a light fall of snow, the gophers run their tunnels directly upon the surface of the ground, appropriating to their uses as they go the stems of grasses and other plants.

Very often the earth composing both the winter cores and the summer mounds is quite different in appearance from that of the superficial layers of the ground immediately underneath them. This makes such "workings" very conspicuous, as they are, with reference to the ground on which they lie, in the relation of a geological unconformity.

Rather than being a drawback to the interests of the pocket gopher, the snow seems to be of real benefit. Two factors are here involved. I have referred to the timidity of the animal, and this is doubtless due to the relentless pursuit of it by certain carnivorous mammals and birds with the resultant precautions necessary on the part of the gopher to keep out of sight and reach. The snow provides cover which conceals the rodent effectually from certain of its enemies. At the same time, the vertical range of accessible food sources is greatly increased; for the gopher is able to reach plant stems and leaves enveloped in the snow mantle, many inches and even feet above the ground surface. All this is subject to confirmation through study of the winter workings uncovered at the time of the spring thaw.

Some estimates made by us while carrying on field work near Porcupine Flat, Yosemite Park, will serve to indicate the amount of work done by pocket gophers. It was found that the average amount of earth put up in the form of winter cores was, on a selected area, 1.64 pounds per square yard. Assuming that, on the average, gopher workings covered only one-tenth per cent of the land surface, there would be 3.6 tons of earth put up per square mile, or 4,132 tons over the whole Park. This is for a single winter! It will be recalled that there are many square miles of either solid rock or slide rock in the Park, where gophers cannot work. On the other hand, in favorable localities workings occur on every square yard of surface; so that it is believed that the average of one-tenth per cent is conservative for the Park as a whole. In summer the amount of material excavated is probably at least as great as that in winter—exactly how much has not yet been determined. For the year, Mr. Storer and myself feel safe in doubling the total figure just given, which, in another unit of measure, would be close to 160 carloads of 50 tons each. We estimate further that the earth to the above amount is lifted by the gophers an average distance of about eight inches; 5500 foot-tons of energy are expended by these little animals in Yosemite Park during a single year.

The question then presents itself as to the general effect of all this work upon the terrain at large, and further upon the vegetation and even upon the animal life of the region. I will proceed to enumerate some of these relations which seem to be borne by pocket gophers to their environment.

(1) The weathering of the substratum is hastened by the burrow systems carrying the air and the water and contained solvents to the subsoil particles and rock masses below.

(2) The sub-soil is comminuted and brought to the surface where it is exposed to further, and increased rate of, weathering.

(3) The loose earth brought up and piled on the surface of the ground thereby becomes available for transportation by wind and water; rain and melted snow carry it from the slopes down to fill up glacial depressions and to make meadows of them; and when these are full, the sediment is carried on still farther by the gathering streams to contribute to the upbuilding of the great and fertile valleys beyond the foothills.

(4) Water is conserved for the reason that snow melts more slowly on porous ground than on hard-packed soil or bare rock, so that the spring run-off is retarded and the supply to the streams below is distributed over a longer period of time; furthermore, the porous soil retains the water longer than packed ground and gives it up with corresponding slowness. Spring floods are less liable to occur and a more regular water supply is insured to the lowlands.

(5) A porous, moist soil produces a fuller vegetational cover—forest, brushland and meadow—and this again favors water conservation.

(6) The ground is rendered more fertile through the loosening of the soil as well as through the permeation of it by the tunnels themselves, thereby admitting both air and water to the roots of the plants; the mineral constituents of the soil become more readily available, and the rootlets are better able to penetrate the earth.

(7) The accumulated vegetational débris on the surface of the ground is eventually buried by the soil brought from below by the gophers, and becomes incorporated to form the humus content so favorable for the successful growth of most kinds of plants.

My readers will have been reminded by a portion of the above considerations, of Darwin's classical study of the relation of earthworms to soil formation. There is undoubtedly a parallel here, the more significant in that the earthworm is a relatively rare animal in California; and what earthworms there are here, are of small size, and of relative inconsequence in effect upon the soil. The pocket gopher is wonderfully equipped to handle the refractory young soils of the semi-arid Sierran slopes, and his rôle here is, in a way, that of Darwin's earthworm in England.

The greatest of all agencies of erosion in the Sierra Nevada, the glaciers, so stressed by John Muir, have now ceased to operate, and the less obvious agencies come into prominence. The element of time granted, we are able to conceive of vast accomplishments on the part of even so humble a contributor as the pocket gopher. Gophers have been at work as gophers of modern type since Miocene times. Professor Andrew C. Lawson thinks that the Sierran block had not begun to up-tilt until early Pliocene. Gophers have probably been at work on at least the lower slopes a good share of the entire time occupied in the uplift of the Sierra Nevada.

As in the case of Darwin's earthworms, there is plentiful evidence in California as to the function of burrowing rodents in burying large objects, such as rocks and logs. Ground squirrels and pocket gophers both show an inclination toward placing their nesting chambers beneath objects that will protect them from being dug out by burrowing enemies, such as badgers and coyotes. The earth is taken out from beneath a rock or a boulder by the rodents and deposited around the margin of the object, which thus, as the years go by, gradually disappears, as a result of the process of undermining and settling plus that of the building up of the ground round-about. The seeker need not go far to find good cases of this kind. Mr. Joseph Dixon cites the case of a rock pile on one corner of his ranch which was half buried in ten years. One certain rock settled six inches in comparison with the general land level, during a period of ten years.

Some idea of the extent of the work which gophers have accomplished through time may be gained from the following considerations. There are 33 species and subspecies of this type of burrowing rodent now in existence in California; these are all in a general way similar to one another, but each has distinctive characters which involve not only external features of color and quality of pelage but also internal structures, more especially those of the skull and teeth. These latter features, it will be observed, have to do with the digging equipment which to the gopher is of such vital importance. These characters of skull and teeth are the ones chiefly depended upon by systematic students in determining species. A remarkable thing is that no two of the 33 species occurring in California exist in any one locality. Just one kind lives in a place, to the exclusion of all other kinds. There is probably close correlation of structure with peculiarities of the terrain, as for instance, those shown by loamy, sandy and rocky soils.

Now the remains of gophers' skulls are found in abundance in the Rancho La Brea deposits near Los Angeles. The exact horizon in which they are found is that in which are also found the saber-toothed tiger, the ground sloth, camels, mastodons, and dire wolves. That horizon has been assigned to the Pleistocene epoch; and geologists have estimated that the time elapsed since the deposit of the materials representative of that horizon is to be computed in "tens and even hundreds of thousands of years." A remarkable thing is that a study I have just made of the gophers of Rancho La Brea in comparison with the species existing in the same vicinity today, shows they are identical in every respect.* In, say, two hundred thousand years there has been no modification of the same structures which at the present day vary from place to place to such an extent as to have led this group to be characterized by some zoologists as extraordinarily "plastic." The true inference here is that the processes of divergent evolution, as well as of monotypic evolution, have been exceedingly slow. This however, is somewhat beside the issue.

If we are to grant that gophers have been in existence, carrying on their digging operations for so short a time, geologically, as two hundred thousand years, even then the total amount of turn-over of the ground has been enormous. At the rate determined on one tract of land to be one-tenth of an inch per year, it would in that period of time have amounted to 1700 feet. This is equivalent to 3400 plowings to a depth of six inches.

Computations of this sort may be carried on endlessly, and it is rather good fun to do so for a while; but beyond certain limits, they are not particularly profitable. In this case, especially, there is a wide margin of inaccuracy when an attempt is made to apply the initial figure over large areas.

---

* The species and *subspecies* is *Thomomys bottæ pallescens.*

Interestingly enough our studies have shown that the average depth at which pocket gophers run their burrows beneath the surface of the ground is six inches. And this, I am informed by Prof. John S. Burd, is the usual depth reached by the farmer of California when he plows the land for his crops. Not only does the gopher bring raw soil to the surface to further weathered, thus releasing the mineral food that the plants require, but it is continually burying vegetation beneath the earth which it throws up at the mouths of its burrows; and furthermore, vegetation is cut into pieces and carried below-ground in large quantities by gophers, much of which is not eaten but remains there, just as does the vegetation which is turned under by the plow, to add to the humus content of the soil. All the excreta of a pocket gopher are deposited underground in special branches of its tunnel system, also at about the same critical depth—six inches. The nitrogenous supply from this animal is thus not wasted in any such proportion as it is in the case of those herbivores which live altogether on the surface of the ground. It must be emphasized that it is on *wild* land, land that is untouched by the farmer, that the gophers thus serve in a valuable way as enrichers of the soil.

While the gopher and ground squirrel when they eat grass admittedly come into direct competition with horses, cattle and sheep, the story does not stop there. An important function, it seems to me, performed by burrowing animals is that of counteracting the packing effect of large mammals on uncultivated grazing lands. The impact of heavy feet on the soil, especially when wet, crowds the particles together and renders the earth less suitable for plant growth. Close tamping tends to exclude the air and hence to suffocate the plant roots, to which oxygen is as essential as it is to animal life. One has but to observe the conditions on mountain meadows outside the limits of National parks, to appreciate the point here made. Often where the country has been overstocked with cattle or domestic sheep, the grasslands have become poor—the crop of grass is scrawny—*except* where gopher workings occur; the sites of these are marked by patches of vivid green. Indeed, on ordinary hill slopes I have repeatedly noted the rejuvenation of the plant-cover here and there, traceable directly and obviously to the activity of burrowing rodents. Before the advent of the white man with his cattle and horses a similar service was rendered, though in lesser degree, perhaps, because of the less need for it, when the deer, mountain sheep and bears frequented the same areas.

The question of damage to forests under natural conditions, for example, injury to young trees, is one that has been raised by foresters. There is no doubt but that gophers and squirrels do girdle or cut off the stems of many seedlings and thus terminate the existence of numerous individual trees. But the great number of seedlings observable on parts of any forest floor, vastly more than could ever reach maturity, would seem to indicate that an adjustment in this direction had been reached long ages ago. Plants in general provide for a rate of replacement sufficient to meet the maximum probabilities of casualty, this involving all stages from the seed to the mature fruiting plant.

In the arable lowlands of California the pocket gopher is well-nigh universally, and of course there rightly, condemned for pursuing his activities, in making his living, on lands that have been appropriated and cultivated by man. There, man has disturbed the original balance of natural relations between plants and animals; he aims to make the land produce crops of selected plants in the largest measure possible, and to that end he cultivates the ground himself by very effective "artificial" means. He naturally resents the levy upon the land and its products by any other animal. Most of the original quota of herbivorous mammals has been crowded out by his methods; but the gopher and ground squirrel have been able to persist under the changed conditions. Man's crops have even increased their food resources; and they have been able to cope with the other changes. It is clear that we have here, most surely, a *reversal* of the relationships obtaining in the wild. On wild land there *is* no cultivation in the "artificial" sense. The crops of wild plants—grasses, herbs, shrubs and even trees—depend upon whatever favorable agencies operate in natural ways. The happy relation found by our pioneers was the result of eons of adjustment among all of the elements concerned.

We grant that the farmer must combat the gopher and ground squirrel in his fields and gardens; we sympathize with him for yearning for the total eradication of the rodents there; and we will help him in every conceivable way to control them. But we do not agree with the policy of wholesale extermination advocated by some persons for all areas alike. We hold that our native plant life, on hill and mountainside, in canyon and mountain meadow, would soon begin to depreciate, were the gopher population completely destroyed. Not that such a thing is at all possible; but that it should not be thought of, even, by any intelligent person who seeks to interpret nature correctly. Much less should public money be spent for such a purpose. On wild land the burrowing rodent is one of the necessary factors in the system of natural well-being.

A Possible Function
of the Whiteness of the Breast in
Crevice-searching Birds

IN REVIEWING one's field experience with birds, certain
species are likely to stand out in memory by reason of their
striking color, behavior, or voice, or of two or even all three of
these features in combination. A person of an enquiring turn
of mind will be led to ponder over the possible significance of
these conspicuous features, and he will "gain merit," intellec-
tually, by so doing, even if he never finds himself ready to offer
a conclusive explanation.

At the moment of writing, I have vividly in mind the Dotted
Canyon Wren (*Catherpes mexicanus punctulatus*), a bird met
with, never in large numbers, but under circumstances which
as a rule concentrate attention upon it. Let the reader, with me,
recall this bird in its normal surroundings. Our first glimpse
is likely to be of a fleeting avian figure, seen momentarily in
a remote recess of a broken cliff face or of a rock slide. The bird
may disappear for minutes at a time. By patiently waiting, one
may again see the bird, barely indicated in the gloom of some
cavern. What one then sees is a spot of white moving jerkily
up and down, and this way and that.

We should here recollect the general coloration of the Canyon Wren as seen in full view close at hand. It is solidly dark
brown, save for the brilliant white throat and chest. This expansive white area is well set off by the otherwise dark hue of
the body. In shadow, the dark contour of the bird as seen in
front or from the side vanishes, and there remains, reflecting
what little light there is, the satiny white of the foreparts. And
the "nervous" mannerism of the bird—the spasmodic squat and
recovery and the side-to-side swing—means the abrupt movement of this white area in such a manner as to quickly attract
the attention of an observer.

The interpretation which would most generally be offered for this combination of large contrasting white chest with dark inclosing area is that of a "directive" marking. By its means individuals of a family would be quickly apprised of one another's presence. This directive marking would be particularly useful in the case of a family of young still dependent for food upon their parents. The crevices in the rock faces, of course, provide the food materials. It is to the advantage of the family that the young keep in close touch with their foraging parents, so as quickly to receive the food items retrieved.

I am quite ready to concede the "directive" value of the Canyon Wren's scheme of coloration, and would emphasize its value under the conditions of shadow in which the birds normally forage. It has occurred to me, however, that there is another significance of the white breast, a value not in conflict with the one just indicated, and this value is realized by each individual bird independently of its associates and throughout the year. This is in the *reflection* of whatever light there may be *from* the white throat and chest *into* the small chinks and crannies of the rock surface which the bird is scrutinizing; in other words, the brilliant white has an *illuminating* effect upon the surface that is being searched for minute objects. A further factor enters, that of movement. The bird is continually facing this way and that, which means the shifting of the shadows of small objects on the background, correspondingly, that way and this. The rounded surface of the bird's foreparts means that *some* light is caught and reflected, whatever the bird's position relative to the direction of the outside daylight. Practically anywhere that the bird can see at all, its white area would thus help it to distinguish small objects. One can test the principle apparently here involved by twisting a piece of white paper around his finger and trying out the illuminating effect on the wall in a photographic dark-room, where a limited shaft of daylight is allowed to enter.

We can go farther, and find other instances of the utilitarian scheme of coloration here seemingly in evidence. Think of other shade and crevice hunters: the Bewick Wren, the Creepers, the White-breasted Nuthatch, and certain Woodpeckers.

The constitutionally skeptical, of course, will immediately come back with citations of other wrens, nuthatches, and woodpeckers which have dull or dark-colored breasts. Entirely different factors may, however, in such cases come into play, modifying the situation altogether. I believe a fairly sound interpretation of its significance can be found for practically every feature or combination of features displayed by any animal. In seeking such meanings one is not necessarily guilty of idle or hopeless speculation.

Geography and Evolution

THE POINT of view of any biologist with regard to general questions is bound to be affected in important measure by his own personal experience. This has been said a hundred times before, but merits repeating. The view I shall now set forth as to the manner of evolution is that of a student of faunal and systematic vertebrate zoology. My experience has been further restricted to conditions and materials in western North America, more particularly to those in California. Admittedly, this restriction or *narrowness* of experience may have had baneful influences. At the same time it is believed that some compensation has been derived from the better opportunity thereby afforded of scrutinizing certain groups of facts rather closely.

It is easy to veil ideas by expressing them in words which have a wide range of meaning. So let me designate what *I* mean by the word evolution. I will simply quote Cope, without, however, assenting to all of the implications he set forth. Evolution is "change of specific and superspecific type through time." As to the word "species," I like Doctor Jordan's characterization, that "a species is not merely a form or group of individuals distinguished from other groups by definable features"; it is "a kind of animal or plant which has run the gauntlet of the ages and *has persisted*." A species in nature, I would emphasize, is not any sort of a variant strain, even one of the more striking mutants, *until* such variant has been subjected to the drastic processes of trial for existence under natural conditions, and *has "stood."*

With regard, again, to the formation and further differentiation of species—the process to which the word evolution applies—this is in my mind a very definite and distinctive thing. Evolution is *not* variation, nor is it inheritance, nor gene-mutation, nor hormone-production, nor any other quality or feature or process, though each and all of these may be vital to the existence and persistence of living beings. Of course, a

[151]

species of animal cannot persist through time without reproduction and inheritance, with their complicated mechanisms,
coming into play. But I can readily conceive of the mere persistence of a species, for a long period, without its undergoing
any modification whatsoever. *Change* of type through time, in
other words, evolution, is an altogether separate phenomenon.

Note that I, as a systematist, insist that the element of *time*
has been involved in the formation of species and subspecies,
as I know them in the wild. I have never found evidence that
would lead me to suppose that any of the existing kinds of
mammals or birds in western America came into being suddenly. There is much good evidence to show that *slow* lapse of
time has accompanied all differentiation.

Since some zoologists may question the relative permanence
of the systematist's subspecies and species, I would call attention to Sumner's experiments with certain wild mice. Sumner
has reared ten or twelve generations of geographic races from
remote and differing areas, under the conditions obtaining at
La Jolla, without any modification in type yet being manifest.
The remains of pocket gophers in the Rancho La Brea deposits
offer a still more significant case. These excellently preserved
skulls of *Thomomys* associated with remains of mammals of
known Pleistocene age show characters identical with not only
the species but the very subspecies existing in the vicinity of
Los Angeles today. In upwards of 200,000 years which, it has
been suggested to me by Doctor Stock, may have elapsed since
those La Brea gophers lived and died, no changes in cranial
features sufficient to be appreciable to the systematist have
taken place.

Lest there be misunderstanding on this point, let me explain
that subspecies and species are identical things, phylogenetically; they differ only in the circumstance that related subspecies intergrade spatially: some feature of surface geography or
in the history of their differentiation has allowed continuous
free intercourse between the differentiating populations, so
that intermediates persist. Between any two "full" species there
is an absolute gap or hiatus.

Observation of species in the wild convinces me that the existence and persistence of species is vitally bound up with environments. The extent and the persistence of a given kind of environment bear intimately upon the fate of the species we find occupying that environment. Environments are forever changing—slowly in units of recent time, perhaps. Yet with relative rapidity they circulate about over the surface of the earth, and the species occupying them are thrust or pushed about, herded as it were, hither and thither. If a given environment be changed suddenly its more specialized occupants disappear—species become extinct.

The facts of geographic distribution, accumulating in very great and increasing amount, demonstrate beyond reasonable doubt that diversity of environments, otherwise habitats, has been essential to the evolution of every one of the many diverse types of vertebrate animals. Evolution of environments came first—comes first; it is going on continually and in a fashion significantly correlated with the gradual modification of the animals themselves. The course of organic evolution has been molded and is being molded by environmental circumstance. In one sense there is directed evolution—orthogenesis of a kind.

In support of this idea I would call attention to the great number of *similar* ecologic types of animals which are developed in widely separated regions and which are derived from *unrelated* stocks. The Kangaroo Rat of our deserts corresponds ecologically to the Jerboa of the Sahara; but it is derived from squirrel ancestry, while the Jerboa is more nearly related to house mice. The Tree-creeper of North America is a true Passerine bird, while the superficially similar Tree-creeper of Patagonia is a Tracheophonine. The various habitats in Australia have produced within the one Mammalian order, Marsupialia, ecologic types which are startlingly similar to many of the mammals of other regions which belong to other orders. This is the "adaptive radiation" of Osborn and many other paleontologists, who find support for their views in an entirely different set of facts than those here emphasized.

Habitats have been variously classified by students of geographical distribution. Some of us have concluded that we can usefully recognize, as measures of distributional behavior, the realm, the region, the life-zone, the fauna, the subfauna, the association, and the ecologic or environmental niche. The latter, ultimate unit, is occupied by just one species or subspecies; if a new ecologic niche arises, or if a niche is vacated, nature hastens to supply an occupant, from whatever material may be available. Nature abhors a vacuum in the animate world as well as in the inanimate world.

Our classification of environments is found not infrequently to relate itself significantly to the phylogeny of animals as ascertained from study of their structure. Within the boundaries of California we recognize at the present moment 418 species and subspecies of mammals, 588 of birds, 80 of reptiles, and 37 of amphibians. This is, by a good margin, the largest vertebrate fauna obtaining in any state in the Union save Texas. The explanation of this abundance of vertebrate species in California (and this holds for Texas in like manner) lies obviously in the diversity of climatic environments which exist within the State. We have extremes in those various factors of the environment to which animal life and plant life are sensitive in marked degree; namely, in temperature, in atmospheric humidity, in rainfall, and in light intensity. A great range in each of these critical factors has produced, in various combinations, a multitude of environments. Opportunities for active speciation have been afforded in the many different geographic units which have developed. New occupants of ecologic niches, new associations, new subfaunas, and new faunas have been molded out of the various biotic materials which happened to be available. New types of living things, to fit into all the new niches, have been evolved, not abruptly but through long lapse of time.

The production of deserts, conditioned by aridity induced by circumstances in the geological and climatological history of the Western Hemisphere, has resulted in many more subspecific, specific, generic, and possibly even family types coming into being than would have been the case had conditions of aridity not arisen; and these new divergencies will have influence in world evolution in that they are supplying a much wider range of materials for further selection—for preservation and improvement of, perhaps, new adaptive structures in the history of life.

My concept of the way in which these developments have taken place is somewhat as follows. Stocks have been isolated under peculiar and differing sets of conditions. Differentiation of these stocks has ensued; invasion has come about, because of the centrifugal pressure of growing populations; migration of the young races has taken place by reason of the movement of the boundaries of geographic units, in other words, of barriers; and the subsequent re-invasion, by the further differentiated stocks, of areas inhabited by their ancestors has taken place. This process, of *evolution,* has involved time and space concurrently.

I believe that isolation has been an essential factor in evolution, though not to the extent, perhaps, that some students have maintained. In my interpretation, isolation alone has not sufficed; stocks, in vertebrates at least, must have been set apart under different sets of conditions for isolation to be effective.

Geographic segregation, isolation, is variously effective; for example, in proportion to the length of time involved; also, in proportion to the degree of completeness of the isolation, for there can be more or less complete separation of stocks, incomplete separation resulting in subspecies. Size of area in which approximate uniformity of conditions prevails is an important circumstance; a large area brings conspicuous results when a small area does not, because of the swamping effects when populations are closely adjacent. In the case of incompleteness of isolation, the distance apart of centers of proliferation of populations modifies rate of differentiation. There are very obvious differences in plasticity or amenability to modification on the part of different species. The presence of this intrinsic factor in many cases strikes the student of speciation forcibly.

There is a human element, too, concerning the nature of the characters which are capable of recognition by the student of species; some characters he can see readily; others perhaps even more important phylogenetically, tend to be overlooked.

There is, of course, the *biotic* environment of any species, apart from the inanimate or physical environment, to be considered—often very important in the adaptive modifications wrought upon the species. Food in kind and quantity, breeding places of a proper sort, and appropriate cover or protection for individuals, are each and all conditions of existence which are influenced in important measure not only by the vegetation of the habitat of a vertebrate species, but by the animal associates of that species. These associates include predacious enemies, parasites, competitors for food or shelter, all manner of living things which bear upon the fate of the individual and therefore influence the career of the species. But these biotic elements in the general environment are, I would urge, in final analysis controlled in *their* kinds and proportions, and often in similar degree, by the physical forces concerned with "geography."

The only mechanism of which I have ever heard, that I can reasonably conceive as operating to permit of the molding of species under the stress of environments is natural selection. It is natural selection that not only at least helps to differentiate initial stocks; natural selection determines absolutely which of two or more differentiated stocks shall survive. Natural selection, in the matter of world evolution, has operated much more conspicuously upon subspecies, species, and higher groups than it has upon individuals. The course of the history of all types living today has been accompanied by vast trial and discard of subspecies, species, genera, families, and even orders. Extinctions to persistencies have been as 10,000 to 1.

To summarize: The factors which have caused and directed organic evolution, and which continue to do so, are bound up in the evolution of environments. It is immaterial just how variations arise. Evolution has not begun until trial begins.

Since, therefore, organic evolution is the result of the inter-
action of organic life and diversifying environments, a study
of geographical distribution and adaptation is, in at least the
vertebrate animals, necessary to an understanding of the causes
and methods of evolution.

Bird Netting as a Method in Ornithology

A CHAIN of circumstances, fortuitous as far as I, the reporter, am concerned, has prompted me to give the following recital, and, in particular, has put at my command the material for some inductions that may prove of interest to serious ornithologists.

On October 21, 1923, Deputy John Burke of the California State Fish and Game Commission for San Mateo County, arrested four "Italians" for the illegal killing of song birds. The birds had been taken by netting, and they and the five nets were confiscated. By instruction of Mr. J. S. Hunter, Assistant Executive Officer of the Fish and Game Commission, the birds, numbering 133, were, on the next afternoon, brought over to Berkeley by Deputy Burke and turned over to the custody of the California Museum of Vertebrate Zoology, to put to whatever scientific use might seem desirable.

In conversation with Deputy Burke, whose headquarters are at Daly City, San Mateo County, California, I learned that he had seen the men on their way to the field of their operations, had suspected their purpose, and, after giving them sufficient time to get into action, had descended upon them, gathering in the men and their whole outfit. The entire lot of birds had been captured within a period of 1½ hours and had been taken in one ravine, opposite Holy Cross Cemetery, just over the San Mateo County line from San Francisco. It is my impression, from what Deputy Burke said, that the capture had been made at one drive, or setting of the nets, in a shallow, brushy "draw." However, as will be explained later, I was unable to verify any of these points. At the time of the conversation I was counting on full opportunity to learn first-hand the methods used by "Italians" to net birds.

Subsequently, the four defendants were arraigned, convicted, and fined in the aggregate $450.00—which amounted to $3.38 for each bird taken. (See Calif. Fish and Game, vol. 10, January, 1924, p. 35.) The nets were, at last accounts, still in the custody of the Fish and Game Commission, though it was hinted that they would eventually be destroyed.

The 133 dead birds were counted and checked at the Museum on the afternoon of October 22, and the work of preparing as many of them as possible as specimens was immediately begun. As a result, 87 were "saved" and are now duly catalogued as part of the scientific collections of the Museum of Vertebrate Zoology. Those preserved include all on the following list except most of the Golden-crowned Sparrows and some of the Nuttall's Sparrows.

List of species, with age and sex recorded as far as ascertained:

Nuttall's Sparrow (*Zonotrichia leucophrys nuttalli*), 21 ad. (7 ♂ ♂, 13 ♀ ♀, saved), 41 im. (3 ♂ ♂, 6 ♀ ♀, saved)..................................... 62
Intermediate Sparrow (*Zonotrichia leucophrys gambeli*), ♀ ad., ♂ im...... 2
Golden-crowned Sparrow (*Zonotrichia coronata*), only three dissected, two of them im. ♂ ♂, the other an im. but sex in doubt.................... 16
Santa Cruz Song Sparrow (*Melospiza melodia santaecrucis*), ad., 6 ♂ ♂, 5 ♀ ♀; im., 18 ♂ ♂, 9 ♀ ♀... 38
Northeastern Lincoln's Sparrow (*Melospiza lincolni lincolni*), ♀ im........ 1
Forbush's Lincoln's Sparrow (*Melospiza lincolni gracilis*), ♀ ad., ♂ im., ♀ im. 3
Swamp Sparrow (*Melospiza georgiana*), ♀ im........................... 1
Yakutat Fox Sparrow (*Passerella iliaca annectens*), 2 im. ♀ ♀............. 2
San Francisco Spotted Towhee (*Pipilo maculatus falcifer*), 4 im. ♂ ♂....... 4
Dusky Warbler (*Vermivora celata sordida*), ♀ im....................... 1
Audubon's Warbler (*Dendroica auduboni auduboni*), ♂ im............... 1
Vigors' Bewick's Wren (*Thryomanes bewicki spilurus*), ♂ ad.............. 1
Coast Bush-tit (*Psaltriparus minimus minimus*), ♀ ad.................... 1

Total... 133

Determination of age was made, as usual, upon the basis of degree of ossification of the skull, except with the Nuttall's Sparrows not skinned out when plumage was depended upon, a seemingly reliable criterion in that species. As judged from the above record (84 immatures to 27 adults), it would appear that in passeriform birds, in October, seventy-five per cent of the general population consists of birds-of-the-year. This inference is probably more nearly correct than would be obtained from records of species in which age is not determinable at a distance, as shot by the average collector; for the method of netting—driving birds up a ravine into a series of set nets— would probably give a much fairer sample of the population. It is probable that in shooting during the autumn, when presumably no vestige of concern of parents for young remains, the larger proportion of adult, experienced birds keeps out of range, and that the tendency would thus be for the "bag" to contain a considerable excess of young birds over their real proportions.

The proportion of the sexes among birds-of-the-year (30 males to 21 females) as compared with that obtaining among adult birds (14 males to 21 females) in so far as it goes shows that, as in human populations, males exceed females in number in the younger period, the case reversing as age advances.

A striking feature in this haul by aerial nets is the presence in it of species of birds which the ordinary collector, by the shooting method, would probably have failed altogether to detect. The Swamp Sparrow (no. 44089, Mus. Vert. Zool.) constitutes the second known occurrence for the State, the only previous record (see Dickey, 'Condor', xxiv, 1922, p. 136), being from Lone Pine, in Owens Valley, east of the Sierra Nevada; and the westernmost record preceding that is from Arizona (Howell, 'Condor', xviii, 1916, p. 213). The presence of the Dusky Warbler (no. 44096, Mus. Vert. Zool.), though this bird has previously been recorded in the San Francisco Bay region, is of sustained interest because the nearest known breeding ground of the race lies on the Santa Barbara Islands, 260 miles, at nearest, to the southward. This additional record makes still more probable the regularity of a northward autumnal movement of at least a part of the population.

It may be inferred, provisionally, that, in the floral association in which the haul of the nets was made, namely, a sort of low chaparral, and at the season specified, small birds occur in the proportions shown in the above list. Thus, it would appear that the Nuttall's Sparrow is far and away the dominant species in the resident category there, and that the Golden-crowned Sparrow is the dominant species among winter visitants. There are only one-fourth as many non-resident as resident birds (27 to 106). Ninety-seven per cent of the total individuals are graminivorous or herbivorous, leaving only three per cent that are insectivorous—in this particular association at this particular season of the year. These are significant figures upon the supposition that we have here a fairer "sample" of the general population, less "selective" at least, than would have been afforded by shooting or by current banding procedure. At the same time, I must urge, again, the inadequacy of one single haul of the nets to establish really conclusive generalizations. A long series of hauls, only, would suffice.

The above comments show some ways in which wholesale sampling of bird populations would bring out important facts. Now as to method: I, personally, prepared 62 of the birds. In only one out of this number did I find any marked evidence of internal injury. There was nothing that would show that any bird had been killed by pressure on the back of the skull or by neck-wringing. I do not know *how* the birds were killed. Furthermore, despite the fact that this mass of birds had been piled in together and transported in a suitcase along with five nets and some other things, the plumage, after the birds were singled out, showed little mussing. In very few of the specimens were wing or tail feathers missing or even permanently bent. The service of these netted birds as specimens was consequently far ahead of what would have been the case with a similar number of birds shot. There was not a shattered bill in the lot, no broken tarsi, no shot-cut feathers.

Again, in attempting to discuss method, I am in the dark on several important points. I should like to have known if birds that got away (if any) were injured. The collector, just as in the case of the hunter of game, must admit that a certain percentage of the birds he shoots at are not retrieved, and that very few of those hit likely recover from their wounds. In other words, in shooting there is a regular wastage of birds, consisting of individuals which do not drop dead but which fly off out of sight, to die sooner or later from the effects of their wounds, or to be snapped up by predators because of their weakened condition. The question of relative humaneness of method might well come up here, in addition to the purely economic one of wastage.

As all these points in favor of using the netting method for scientific purposes dawned upon me, the desire naturally grew to try it out. On October 25, 1923, I petitioned the Assistant Executive Officer of the State Fish and Game Commission for the transfer of the confiscated nets to the custody of the University of California "as objects of interest and instruction," and, furthermore (a separate proposition), for the purpose of operating them myself, under instruction of some "Italian," to capture birds for scientific purposes. I stated that in operating the nets, only scientifically desirable birds would be "collected," the balance liberated. Also, I suggested the testing out of the netting method as a means of capturing, banding and releasing birds in the general campaign of bird-banding now in vogue.

In reply, surprise was expressed by the Fish and Game representative at my "audacity." My petition was not granted. I wrote again on November 26, 1923, and on January 15, 1924. I was put off, without any better reason than that, if my proposal were met favorably, a bad example would be set to "Italians." And I may say, further, that I proposed the same thing verbally to an official of the United States Department of Agriculture— with exactly the same reaction! It would be wrong to *net* birds, because (I gathered) alien "Italians" do it, when they can, to get birds to eat. I fail to see the logicality of this point of view. The same line of reasoning would make it wrong to *shoot* either game birds out of season or non-game birds at any time, *under permit,* for scientific specimens—because of the possible "example" set to unprincipled Americans (and there *are* such) who would thereupon go out and shoot birds, just for the sport of it if not to eat. I am unable, personally, to see that *method* of capture makes any difference whatsoever, on the score of "example." Permits *are,* and properly so, issued for the taking of birds for scientific purposes. The *way* of "taking" them is hardly material.

It is very likely that there is a considerable Old World literature on the subject of bird netting. In certain European countries, I understand, netting for the market has been a fixed custom for centuries. And it would likely be an aid if this literature could be sought out for "helpful hints" in the operation of nets!

Seriously, the possibilities in netting birds for banding loom up. The avowed aim of bird banders, under the leadership of the Biological Survey, is to band birds in *quantity*—the more the better. Achievement of the objects of bird banding, objects urged on the ground of their scientific value, are to be realized upon in direct proportion to the quantity of birds banded. There is no gainsaying this, surely. This thing of trapping birds one by one or, at best, a few of them at a time, is relatively hopeless as bearing on problems of migration when one considers the slim chances of re-capture. To say it another way, the chances of re-capture are to be increased directly as the number of bandings is increased. The method of netting, which the "Italians" can teach us if we grasp the opportunity to be taught, is the only adequate wholesale method in the banding campaign that has yet been suggested for the usual run of small land-birds. In human history it is, of course, nothing novel that hands should be held up in holy horror at the idea of adopting something new. "It isn't done," however, is hardly a scientific ground for turning down so promising a method in ornithology as bird netting, intelligently conducted, would seem to be.

The foregoing discussion may seem unnecessarily aspersive in places. I admit my proneness to aspersiveness, and submit apology for allowing my weakness such full play in the present connection. My only excuse is that by so doing I may have made certain worthwhile ideas the more impressive.

A Conservationist's Creed as to Wild-Life Administration

(1) I BELIEVE that the fullest use should be made of our country's wild life resources from the standpoint of human benefit—for beauty, education, scientific study, recreation, for sport, for food, for fur, etc. *All* these possible uses should be considered in the administration of wild life, not any one of them exclusively of the others. At the same time, any one use may be of more importance than the others in a given locality, so that such locality may be administered with that particular value most prominently in view.

(2) I believe that that portion of our wild animal life known as "game" belongs no more to the sportsman than to other classes of people who do not pursue it with shotgun and rifle. More and more the notebook, the field glass and the camera are being employed in the pursuit of game as well as other animals. The newer generation by hundreds of thousands is turning to nature-out-of-doors, for recreation, instruction and pleasure through such agencies as the national parks, summer camps, Boy Scouts, Girl Scouts and Camp Fire Girls. Indeed, these other claimants upon our "game" resources are probably reaching to numbers greater than those of active sportsmen; *their* rights certainly deserve at least equal consideration.

(3) I believe it is unwise to attempt the absolute extermination of any native vertebrate species whatsoever. At the same time, it *is* perfectly proper to reduce or destroy any species in a given neighborhood where sound investigation shows it to be positively hurtful to the majority of interests. For example, coyotes, many rodents, jays, crows, magpies, house wrens, the screech owl and certain hawks may best be put under the ban locally.

(4) I believe it is wrong to permit the general public to shoot crows or any other presumably injurious animals during the

breeding season of our desirable species. It is dangerous to invite broadcast shooting of any so-called vermin during the regular closed season, when the successful reproduction of our valuable species is of primary importance and is easily interfered with.

(5) I believe in the collecting of specimens of birds and vertebrates generally for educational and scientific purposes. The collector has no less right to kill non-game birds and mammals, in such places where he can do so consistently with other interests, than the sportsman has right to kill "game" species. A bird killed, but preserved as a study-specimen, is of service far longer than the bird that is shot just for sport or for food.

(6) I believe that it is wrong and even dangerous to introduce (that is, turn loose in the wild) alien species of either game or non-game birds and mammals. There is sound reason for believing that such introduction, if "successful," jeopardizes the continued existence of the native species in our fauna, with which competition is bound to occur.

(7) I believe that the very best known way to "conserve" animal life, in the interests of sportsman, scientist and nature-lover, alike, is to preserve conditions as nearly as possible favorable to our own native species. This can be done by the establishment and maintenance of numerous wild-life refuges, not only as comprised in private and public parks, but in national forests and elsewhere.

(8) In the interests of game and wild life conservation generally, I believe in the wisdom of doing away with grazing by domestic stock, more especially sheep, on the greater part of our national forest territory. A further, and vital, interest bound up in this factor is the conservation of water.

(9) I believe that the administration of our game and wild life resources should be kept as far as possible out of politics. The appertaining problems are essentially biological ones and are fraught with many technical considerations not appreciated or understood by the average politician or sportsman. The resources in question should be handled as a national asset, administered with the advice of scientifically trained experts.

Geography and Evolution
in the Pocket Gopher

THE MOST universally distributed type of rodent in California is the pocket gopher. It is found thriving at and below sea level, around the southern end of Salton Sea in Imperial County, and above timber line, at 11,500 feet altitude in the vicinity of Mount Whitney; it is found from the arid desert mountain ranges of the Inyo region, such as the Panamint Mountains, to the rainy and foggy coast strip at Humboldt Bay and Crescent City; it is found in the yielding sands of the Colorado River delta at the Mexican line and on the Modoc lava beds at the Oregon line.

This fact of occurrence far and wide might seem to indicate a broad tolerance, tolerance of a number of conditions each varying between wide extremes. How is such an interpretation to be harmonized with the obvious fact that the pocket gopher is an exceedingly specialized type of rodent? Does not specialization ordinarily bring great restriction in habitat? A truism is this statement: The pocket gopher stock has solved successfully the problem of meeting the essential conditions of existence, else its racial line would not have persisted to the present day. Among races of animals the law is evident that only those budding forms persist and continue to evolve that are able to find suitable places, niches for themselves, in the economy of animal existence that are not already preëmpted and successfully occupied by other forms.

The pocket gophers are rodents restricted to the Western Hemisphere; not only that, they comprise a family (*Geomyidae*) restricted to the continent of North America; furthermore, that family centers in the southern half of the continent. The family *Geomyidae* contains several subdivisions—genera in the parlance of the systematist. The genus *Thomomys*, to which all the gophers of California belong, is still further restricted to that portion of North America lying altogether west of the Mississippi River, and between the 20th and 55th degrees of latitude. As to origin, pocket gophers are of squirrel-like ancestry. But that was in very remote times, geologically speaking: for the particular genus *Thomomys* has been in existence since the Miocene period. Despite this long lapse of time, then, the group of rodents here under consideration has not found its way beyond certain geographic limits, and yet within those limits it is exceedingly abundant and widespread, in other words, successful. What was the place for itself that the nascent ancestral race, just becoming gopher-like, discovered and which its descendants, continually specializing, have found so favorable?

Superficial examination of a garden gopher shows the animal to be remarkably formed throughout for existence underground. Observation of its habits shows that in all probability each individual spends fully 99 per cent of its time underground. Its world is limited by the earthen walls of a burrow which the animal is equipped to dig for itself through the soil. In one direction this burrow leads to safety for itself and young, from enemies; at the other end it makes food accessible. Thus the conditions of existence for any vertebrate animal, safe refuges and breeding places, and food of right kind and sufficient amount, are met.

But this discovery of a previously unappropriated means of subsistence, by adoption of the subterranean mode of life, has brought with it deficiencies in certain faculties not bound up with proficiency in digging. To dig, the animal must have short legs and a muscular body, especially anteriorly. The head of a pocket gopher is larger in proportion to its body than is that of any other land mammal in California; there is no obvious neck constriction, and the shoulders are broad. The musculature having to do with the operation of the front feet is massive; and so also are the bones of the skull to which are attached the big muscles which operate the relatively heavy incisor teeth, these being the chief tools with which the gopher loosens the soil as it advances along its underground routes of exploration for food, or digs to greater depths for more secure refuge. Obviously, the acquisition of all these modifications for burrowing has necessitated the loss of that litheness of body and length of limb which would enable it to move freely over the surface of the ground in search of food or in escape from enemies. The pocket gopher is, indeed, wellnigh lacking in powers of locomotion overland.

Furthermore, the pocket gopher is deficient relatively to other rodents with respect to eyesight, and probably also with respect to hearing. It is almost as helpless outside its burrow as a fish out of water. There may be some compensation in a heightened sense of touch, especially as localized in the nose and surrounding vibrissae and in the tip of the tail. While the animal has little need of being apprised of goings-on outside the walls of its tunnel, it does need to be aware of conditions in front and behind. We find that it moves in its cylinder nearly as well in backward direction as forward.

Since, as seems apparent, the general question of the pocket gopher's occurrence over wide territory must take into account its very special mode of gaining a livelihood, it will be useful in our discussion to inquire further as to its digging proclivities and the structures correlated with these. Comparison of the pocket gopher, as an extreme type of digger, with, say, the California ground squirrel, shows significant differences. While the brain-case has, in the two animals, relatively about the same capacity, the skull of a gopher is four times as heavy as that of a ground squirrel, total weights of the two animals being considered. As indicated above, the skull and teeth of the pocket gopher, together with the muscles which operate them, comprise the chief engine of digging. This engine operates in powerful fashion in cutting away the earth, so as to make possible the rapid extension of the gopher's underground system of passageways. The adequate housing of the heavy incisor teeth, and the need of meeting the severe stresses during the action of the muscles which operate the jaws, have resulted in the great thickening and ridging of the bones of the skull. We find that the forefeet are larger than the hind feet, a reversal of the ratio in animals which can run with agility; and the forefeet are provided with long stout curved claws. The forearm and shoulder are heavily muscled, and thus the actions of the jaws and teeth are supplemented, in loosening and particularly in transporting the soil.

So far as is known, no pocket gopher goes into dormancy at any season; none either aestivates or hibernates. The source of food upon which the pocket gopher can depend, year in and year out, and which it can seek in safety, is comprised in the underground stems and root stalks of various grasses and herbs. These it gets almost altogether by digging its way to them; it gathers food only as it can advance under cover. While it is true that gophers do pull into the temporarily open mouths of burrows, stems and leaves of above-ground plants, these latter, I am led to believe, constitute only a minor fraction of the total annual food supply of the animal. The only dependable food source, continuing throughout the year, is comprised in underground stems and roots. And this is an exceedingly important consideration in our present study; for the general geographic limitation of *Thomomys,* to North America west of the 100th meridian, coincides with the territory where sharp alternation of dry and wet seasons is characteristic of the climate. Linked up with this climatic peculiarity there is undoubtedly, in the Southwest, relatively greater abundance of plants with nutritious roots and thickened underground stems, which tide over the dry season, than in the remainder of North America, where there is no long dry season. In other words, the ancestral pocket gophers of the remote past made the fortunate discovery of an oncoming type of food source correlated with the increasing aridity of what came to be a marked climatic and vegetational province.

Restricting our attention now to *Thomomys* as the genus occurs in California, I will revert to the fact of its well-nigh universal distribution within the State. How can the fact of this wide distribution be harmonized with the restriction in the animal's mode of existence which we have just pointed out in some detail? Examination of the territory wherever pocket gophers thrive, from one end of the State to the other, does show most emphatically close concordance of occurrence with those very, and special, conditions—of suitable food, and of consistency of soil which permits of digging. In other words, these two critical factors *are* widespread, and wherever they extend pocket gophers have gone.

The hindrances, locally, to the spread of pocket gophers are comprised in, not altitude, not cold, not heat, but in discontinuity of ground wherein the pocket gopher can extend its burrows; in discontinuity of ground in which sufficient food of the kind the pocket gopher can use is available throughout the year; and of course, in impassable bodies or streams of water. In other words, we find operating as outright barriers to their distribution only ground such as lava flows which cannot be penetrated by gophers, or ground which is too dry or too alkaline to support adequate plant growth for the gophers' food throughout the year, or permanent streams or bodies of water which the gopher cannot cross.

In this latter connection, the pocket gopher can thrive, we know, without ever drinking; in many parts of the State the only water it can get for long periods is contained in the plant tissues which it uses for food. On the other hand, the animal can live healthily in soil that is saturated with water. Yet it is forced out of the ground when the land is flooded, as during very heavy rains or when under irrigation. Not only a river itself, but the adjacent bottomland subject to overflow at high water, may thus be effective in limiting the spread of gophers locally. A gopher can swim short distances when forced to; but it does not take to water voluntarily. These facts bear on the problem of geographic differentiation of races now to be discussed.

I have pointed out that, despite the pocket gopher's extreme specializations in structure and habits, despite its restriction to a very narrow range of living conditions, yet the fact that these special living conditions are widespread has permitted of the very wide distribution in California, of this type of ro-

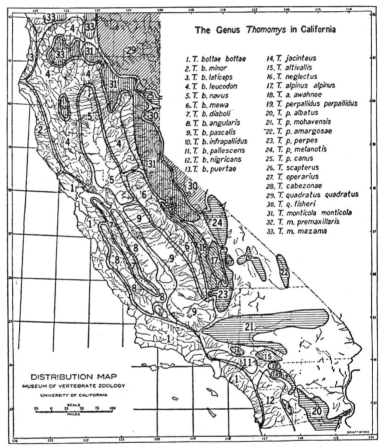

The Genus *Thomomys* in California

1. *T. bottae bottae*	14. *T. jacinteus*
2. *T. b. minor*	15. *T. altivallis*
3. *T. b. laticeps*	16. *T. neglectus*
4. *T. b. leucodon*	17. *T. alpinus alpinus*
5. *T. b. navus*	18. *T. a. awahnee*
6. *T. b. mewa*	19. *T. perpallidus perpallidus*
7. *T. b. diaboli*	20. *T. p. albatus*
8. *T. b. angularis*	21. *T. p. mohavensis*
9. *T. b. pascalis*	22. *T. p. amargosae*
10. *T. b. infrapallidus*	23. *T. p. perpes*
11. *T. b. pallescens*	24. *T. p. melanotis*
12. *T. b. nigricans*	25. *T. p. canus*
13. *T. b. puertae*	26. *T. scapterus*
	27. *T. operarius*
	28. *T. cabezonae*
	29. *T. quadratus quadratus*
	30. *T. q. fisheri*
	31. *T. monticola monticola*
	32. *T. m. premaxillaris*
	33. *T. m. mazama*

DISTRIBUTION MAP
MUSEUM OF VERTEBRATE ZOOLOGY
UNIVERSITY OF CALIFORNIA

SCALE
25   0   25   50   75   100
MILES

Map showing the distribution of the species and subspecies
of pocket gopher in California.

dent. Now we come to deal with the observation that while our pocket gopher as a genus exists in every county of California, from below sea level to almost the highest altitudes, from the hottest to the coldest portions of the State, and from the driest to the wettest belts, yet the *species* represented under all these varying conditions is not the same; the genus is broken up, as indicated on the accompanying map, into not less than 33 different races (species or subspecies), no two of them occupying precisely the same territory. And this fact signifies that the varying combinations of conditions resulting from the topographic and climatic diversity in California *have* made their impress upon the gopher sub-stocks, which are more or less isolated from one another in what may be called differentiation provinces. It is our problem to enquire as to what factors among the present or recently past conditions have resulted in this isolation and consequent differentiation of all these various stocks.

As will be observed from the map, the most conspicuous gopherless areas in California lie in the southeastern desert territory, chiefly on the Mohave Desert. Extended explorations of that arid territory have been made, with the special object of determining the kinds and numbers of rodents and other mammals present. Almost every square mile of those deserts, save on such evaporation floors as those of Searles "Lake" and Panamint and Death valleys (where there is a heavy deposit of saline substances, and no chance of plant growth), supports a large population of *seed*-gathering rodents—kangaroo rats, pocket mice, and ground squirrels of certain species. Throughout all the deserts there *are*, at times, heavy rains, though they may be at intervals of as long as three years; and such rains are followed by luxuriant growths of various herbs. These go to seed and thus give origin to a nutritious type of food, scattered by the winds throughout the drifting sands, to be sought out throughout the long dry intervals by the spermophilous mammals just named. But for the pocket gopher, specialized for gathering, masticating, and digesting roots and stems, and not for seed-gathering, the food resources of the desert are, over most of its extent, inadequate. Only here and there, on mountain tops, where rainfall is more copious and of more regular occurrence than in the surrounding territory, and about permanent springs, is there produced the proper type of vegetation for gopher consumption, in permanent supply.

As a result of these special conditions of food supply, the general distribution of gophers on the deserts is conspicuously *dis*continuous; the animals exist only in colonies here and there, because surrounded by unoccupiable desert; and such colonies are often far isolated from one another. The feeble powers of locomotion of the pocket gophers mean that they are unable to cross the barren intervals, and they are subjected to the same sort of factor, in evolutionary process, as land animals sequestered on islands in the sea. As happens under this circumstance the world over, we find that greater or less degree of inherent, subspecific or even specific, sets of differences characterize the more or less isolated stocks.

As an example of races of pocket gophers which evidently owe their origin to the isolation afforded by discontinuity of food supply, we may cite the form *scapterus* on the Panamint Mountains, which range rises high enough above the general base level of the surrounding desert to enjoy a fairly regular rainfall with a consequent copious growth of biennial or perennial herbs.

Another example, is the race *amargosae*, restricted to the immediate vicinity of the permanent springs in the otherwise dry and alkaline valley of the Amargosa "River," at Shoshone, Inyo County. This quite distinct form, in the *perpallidus* "group" of gophers, may appropriately be looked upon as a relict form from earlier times when conditions of moisture much more generally prevailed in the Great Basin territory, and when the dependent fauna and flora were correspondingly widespread. *Amargosae* is not the only mammal at Shoshone dependent, directly or indirectly, on the presence of permanent water; for there is (or was a few years ago) a distinct race of meadow mouse (*Microtus*) occurring around the same springs. Then the springs themselves contain a unique species of fish, residuary of a stock which evidence shows occurred widely in the general region in former times.

No pocket gopher whatsoever has been found in the depression of Death Valley, into which the Amargosa "River" empties. The lowest parts of the Valley are too intensely alkaline to support any vegetation at all; and such water as there is around the margins, is either too alkaline, too impermanent, or else too small in amount to have permitted the persistence of gophers there up until the present time.

Even such general areas as that indicated on the small-scale map for the race *mohavensis* are not at all continuously occupied by pocket gophers; and examination of representations from different parts of such a general area shows minor differences characterizing the separated colonies. For example, those animals living in the bottomlands of the Mohave River differ slightly from those inhabiting the somewhat higher tablelands surrounding the Providence Mountains, in extreme eastern San Bernardino County.

The Colorado River is significant in our study, in that it has evidently long served as an impassable obstruction to the passage of pocket gopher populations in either direction. The race *albatus,* occupying the delta and "second-bottom" on the western side of the lower course of the Colorado River, is distinctly different in numerous respects, chiefly relating to the skull, from the form *chrysonotus* of the mesa lands on the eastern or Arizona side of the river. The actual distance apart of the nearest populations of these two species is not more than two miles in places, yet the intervening river and its "first-bottom," of ancient existence and large and permanent volume, has acted effectively in preventing the interbreeding of adjacent stocks. Complete isolation accompanied by even slight difference of environments accomplishes much, granted plenty of time.

A puzzle, at first glance, is offered by the occurrence of the two forms, *albatus* in the delta silts below Salton Sea, and *perpallidus* on the floor of the northwestern end of the same (Colorado) desert. Both races are restricted to fine-textured soil in the vicinity of water or where at least some underground seepage permits the proper growth of salt grass and other plants whose stems or roots are sought by gophers. *Albatus* follows the western distributaries of the Colorado River over the delta, and of late has found wonderfully favorable conditions for itself, with resulting enormous spread and multiplication of its numbers, on the irrigated lands of the Imperial Valley. *Perpallidus* occurs chiefly at the mouths of permanent streams coming down the cañons out of the San Jacinto and Santa Rosa mountains onto the floor of the northwestern end of the Colorado Desert, known locally as the Cahuilla Valley. Why should these two races be as distinct as they are from one another when the floor of the general desert area they occupy is continuous, and only about 150 miles in greatest length?

Not long ago, even measuring in years, the northwestern arm of the Colorado Desert was occupied by "Blake Sea," of which the present Salton Sea is the residuum. More remotely yet, the Gulf of California extended continuously up from its present terminus clear through the Cahuilla Valley; and today the floor of that desert is in many places covered with shells of ocean-inhabiting mollusks, and shore lines at sea level are to be seen along the bases of the mountains which rise abruptly on either hand. The rapidly accumulating silts from the Colorado River filled in the depression opposite its mouth and cut off the basin of Blake Sea; and the arid climate resulted in the disappearance of the waters of that sea by evaporation. But completion of this cutting off of Blake Sea and the evaporation of its waters was of quite recent occurrence. We can, I think, look to the former long and complete separation of the gopher stocks resulting in *perpallidus* and *albatus*, respectively, during the period that the waters of Blake Sea, at sea level, lapped the steeply rising rocks on either side impassable to gophers. Complete isolation was thus afforded for the initial bottom-land stocks of gophers at the northwest and to the southeast. With the retraction of the shores of Blake Sea, there is now no barrier between *perpallidus* and *albatus,* save as is comprised in unwatered tracts; and these are getting smaller with the spread of irrigation. It will be interesting to see what happens when and where the two gopher populations meet.

An additional case of isolation by desert conditions is that of *operarius* at Owens Lake, also a member of the *perpallidus* group. *Operarius* is a quite distinct form, so distinct with respect to shape of skull and teeth that individual variation does not bridge over the structural interval between it and its near relative, *perpes*. Hence systematists call it a species, rather than a subspecies, the only criterion for the latter systematic rank being intergradation or blending of its characters with those of another race. *Operarius* is restricted to the vicinity of the permanent springs which occur around the eastern side of Owens Lake in the vicinity of Keeler. There, under conditions of moisture obtaining very locally, there is a luxurious and permanent growth of salt-grass upon which almost exclusively this species of gopher depends for food.

An entirely different *motif,* as one may say, of differentiation is provided on the tops of isolated mountain peaks or ranges. In general, the 33 forms of the genus *Thomomys* in California fall into five "groups," of major systematic significance. These groups probably represent much older periods of differentiation, and the subsidiary forms have budded from each of these major stems. The composition by races and the distribution of each of the five groups is illustrated by the differential shading of the areas of four of them on the accompanying map. The area for the *bottae* group is left unshaded.

It will be observed that three of the groups, which may be called the *bottae, perpallidus,* and *quadratus* groups, respectively, are essentially lowland groups in that they occupy territory of relatively low altitude; while two, the *monticola* and *alpinus* groups, are high-mountain dwelling. In other words, it would appear that some condition associated with altitude has had critical effect in checking the unlimited spread of certain types upward, and of certain other types downward.

Relatively thoroughgoing trapping of gophers along a typical section, transversely, of the Sierra Nevada, in the Yosemite region, shows a sequence of forms by groups from west to east as follows: *pascalis,* of the San Joaquin Valley floor, and *mewa,* of the somewhat higher foothill, digger pine belt, belong to the *bottae* group; *awahnee,* of the *alpinus* group, occupies middle altitudes on the western slope; *monticola,* of the *monticola* group, occupies the whole upper country from about the 6000-foot level to timber line and through the passes and down onto the upper eastern slopes; and at the eastern base of the Sierra Nevada is *fisheri,* of the *quadratus* group. (See accompanying profile, showing correlation with "life zones.") It would ap-

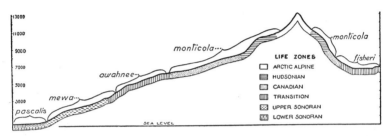

Sectional profile of the Sierra Nevada through the region of Yosemite, showing the location of the species and subspecies of pocket gopher according to altitude and life zone.

pear from this sequence of forms that temperature does, after all, in some measure, constitute a factor bearing critically upon the successful existence of, and hence determining the geographical limitation of, these several species and subspecies of pocket gophers. It might be supposed that relatively uniform temperatures would everywhere surround an animal staying below-ground; but a fact bearing on this suggestion is that the high-mountain gophers all winter do extensive burrowing *through the snow,* thereby reaching in safety stems of plants above the ground surface!

Returning now to the subject of isolation of high-mountain types on disconnected mountain masses, interesting examples are afforded on the highest mountains of southern California by members of the *alpinus* group. These are: *alpinus* in the vicinity of Mount Whitney, *neglectus* on Mount San Antonio of the San Gabriel range, *altivallis* on the San Bernardino Mountains, and *jacinteus* on San Jacinto Peak. As a rule, low-level types of gophers intervene in the low passes between these boreal colonies sequestered as they are by some factor involved in altitude. As a further example of montane sequestration, we find at the north, in the *monticola* group, *premaxillaris* set apart on the Yolla Bolly Mountains. But, curiously, we find *mazama*, of the same group, on the Trinity Mountains and on the Siskiyou Mountains, both these representations without any detectable differences between them, separated by the valley of the Klamath River. This intervening valley is occupied by *leucodon*, a member of the *bottae* group.

With respect to differentiation within the lowland groups, we find an obvious association of the areas of differentiation with difference in climatic humidity—rainfall, or perhaps cloudiness. In this connection, the general northwest-southeast trend of the areas of occupancy of the different members of the *bottae* group is significant. Comparison of this map of gopher distribution with a rainfall map of California shows the parallel. Take an east-west section, gopherwise, from the coast at Santa Cruz, and we find *bottae* inhabiting the narrow, most humid, coastal belt; in the interior San Benito or other valleys, of lesser rainfall, we find *angularis;* on the hard-soiled, juniper-clothed ridges of the Diablo range, is *diaboli;* beyond this on the floor of the San Joaquin Valley, but west of the river, is *angularis* again; to the eastward of the San Joaquin river flood-bottom is *pascalis,* chiefly in the bottomlands of the smaller rivers making down from the Sierras; and higher, on the hard-soiled foothills, is *mewa. Bottae* is darkest colored of all, *pascalis* is palest colored in this series; *bottae* is largest, but *angularis* and *pascalis* are also large; *diaboli* and *mewa* are small, the latter smallest. It would appear that the effects of varying rainfall, or of cloudiness, or of relative humidity of the air, are registered in varying tone of color. And soil texture affects size. The trend of the long, narrow area of occurrence of each of these races happens to be with that of both rainfall belts and mountain axes. The comparative study of the *outlines* of the ranges of animals brings clues as to the essential conditions for the special existence of each.

This matter of coloration of gophers presents a rather baffling problem. Referring to the accompanying plate, which depicts 8 of the 33 gophers of California, it becomes apparent that the paler colored forms are generally associated with arid habitats; the darker colored with humid habitats. *Bottae* of the coast belt as compared with the almost white *albatus* of the Colorado delta presents an extreme amount of difference. Is the factor which has to do with these diverse conditions of coloration, light, or temperature, or is it humidity of the air?

Let us remember that whatever the locality, the pocket gopher stays fully 99 per cent of its time within the underground burrow; and this burrow in desert territory, as well as elsewhere, may run through soil that is nearly or quite saturated with water, though, more often, it must be said, in deserts it extends through soil of relative dryness. In defense of the theory of concealing coloration, it can be urged that the moment of greatest hazard to the animal is the moment when the gopher exposes itself to view at the mouth of its burrow in pushing out earth, even though the total time involved may comprise only a minute a day. It *may* be that the pallor of the desert-inhabiting gopher, like *canus* or *fisheri,* in a statistical majority of cases, brings success in eluding enemies. Not so consistent with this theory is the fact that there are dark-colored gophers which inhabit the white sands of river valleys in relatively humid and cloudy belts; also there are pale gophers in arid territories, which live in very dark-colored soil, as in the case of *fisheri* in parts of the Mono Lake district. While in this particular matter of coloration no immediate explanation of the differences between the races is forthcoming, yet I have confidence that not only this, but each and every other character which we find to distinguish races, has its full adaptive justification in the scheme of existence.

Some reader may ask what grounds I have for assuming that long lapse of time is involved in this process of racial differentiation. Why may not the observed differences be induced rather quickly, in one or a very few generations of gophers,

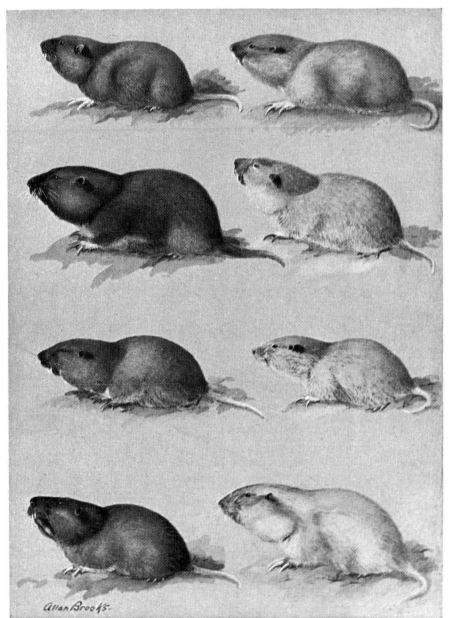

SOME POCKET GOPHERS OF CALIFORNIA

1. *Thomomys monticola mazama*, Trinity Mts., Trinity Co.
2. *Thomomys bottae bottae*, Los Gatos, Santa Clara Co.
3. *Thomomys bottae pascalis*, Lane Bridge, Fresno Co.
4. *Thomomys bottae nigricans*, Witch Creek, San Diego Co.
5. *Thomomys perpallidus canus*, Honey Lake, Lassen Co.
6. *Thomomys perpallidus melanotis*, White Mts., Mono Co.
7. *Thomomys quadratus fisheri*, Walker Lake, Mono Co.
8. *Thomomys perpallidus albatus*, Salt Creek, Imperial Co.

as conditions change locally or as the animals move about, say from one kind of soil into another? In reply: For one thing, we find the animals "true to type," in other words, relatively uniform in characters, each within its own distribution area—and this despite the great local differences in conditions. For example, *bottae* from the grassy tops of the Berkeley Hills is quite like *bottae* from the campus at Stanford University, and quite like *bottae* from the wooded slopes of the Santa Cruz Mountains, and also quite like *bottae* from the sand dunes at Seaside near Del Monte.

For another thing, we have in the Museum of Vertebrate Zoology specimens, skins and skulls, preserved by members of the State Geological Survey sixty years and more ago, representative of several of our Californian races. Compared with specimens of the same races collected today I see no appreciable differences.

And one other line of evidence pointing to the relative permanence of the species and subspecies with which we are dealing: From the Rancho La Brea asphalt deposits near Los Angeles there have been exhumed an abundance of excellently preserved skulls of *Thomomys* intimately associated with remains of certain mammals, now extinct, of known Pleistocene age. And those gophers show cranial characters identical with not only the species *bottae,* but with the subspecies *pallescens* as it exists in the vicinity of Los Angeles today. In other words, in upwards of 200,000 years which it is thought have passed since those Rancho La Brea gophers lived and died, there have been no changes in cranial features such as the systematist would recognize in separating geographic races existing today in different parts of southern California. This adaptive, evolutionary process is one which involves very long periods of time, therefore, when measured in years.

To summarize: In this essay I have set forth some of the facts in the natural history of the pocket gopher. I have picked out for especial comment those features of the animal, as regards both habits and structure, which seem significant in a consideration of its general distribution. I have also emphasized the fact of the differentiation of the pocket gopher type (genus *Thomomys*) in California, into numerous races—species and subspecies. Furthermore, I have referred to the seeming correlation of area of occupancy in each race with relative uniformity of the conditions of existence for that race. The inferior powers of locomotion of this type of rodent, as compared, say, with the jack rabbit, has brought upon it a condition of extreme provincialism, as it were. That is to say, especially with the contributing agency of more or less impassable barriers here and there, each of the many and diverse "gopher differentiation areas" thus formed in California has each impressed its occupant with its *stamp,* namely, a peculiar combination of adaptive characters best fitting that gopher to carry on successful existence in that restricted area. One more inference, of far-reaching implications, fairly forces itself upon us—that evolution of habitats (differentiation areas) must have preceded differentiation of the gopher stocks which came eventually under their impress.

Tree Surgery and the Birds

MY OFFICE is a corner room in the second story. Near the corner of the building stands a large live oak, the nearest one of a scattering group which helps make Faculty Glade. This corner oak extends its branches along either side of the building, so closely that at times of lively breeze the twigs scratch my windows. From within, I can look out among the branches of the tree and up to the under surface of the crown of foliage above.

For eighteen years now, at odd moments day by day, I have watched the birds which visit my corner oak. The total list of species seen, one season and another, has grown to the surprising number of forty-six. Many of these have been only casual or vagrant visitants, of appearance but one or twice. The point of special import now is that I have come to associate each of the regular visitants to this oak with some particular part of the tree. I have become impressed by the instinctive adherence of each kind of bird to trunk, or to larger branches, or to smaller twigs, or to leafage. Indeed, observation here and elsewhere leads me to believe that the presence of a certain kind of perch or particular sort of forage surface is practically essential to the presence of the given kind of bird whose structures and instincts are adapted to it. Moreover, most birds are incapable of quick adjustment to new conditions. Their inherently fixed instincts and structures closely limit them to narrow ranges of conditions. Change unfavorably to even a slight degree the conditions that control their means of subsistence and it becomes impossible for those birds longer to persist in the territory affected.

For two days now 'tree surgeons' have been at work, under directions of a 'landscape architect', upon the trees of Faculty Glade. This morning they reached my corner oak. I have seen the men, with the evident purpose of removing every dead member, and of thinning out the branch-work generally, remove, one after another, particular parts of the tree, parts associated in my memory with the bird-life that has frequented it.

The decaying stub upon which, last year, the Downy Woodpecker drummed, and into which, in the early spring, it essayed to bore for its nest, has fallen before the saw. The long, slanting and crooked branch, with, it is true, but sparse foliage at its end, yet whose bark was searched again and again from one end to the other by a White-breasted Nuthatch, has now been cut off. Another angular branch that was chosen for repeated scrutiny by a vagrant Brown Creeper, the few times I have seen it in the neighborhood, lies on the ground beneath, to be hauled away to the campus trashpile.

A winter's southeaster two years ago broke off, but left suspended in the tangle in the crown of the tree, a branch with its leaves. These leaves, pointing downward, dried and yellowed; but their curled edges seemed to house an inexhaustible supply of desirable things from the standpoint of a pair of Plain Titmouses which took in this objective day after day, as one point in their forage beat. Of course, that pendant spray of dead foliage has had to go.

Just outside the window nearest my desk has been, until today, an arch-shaped twig, unfortunately part of a dying branch. This twig, shaded in part by the building, in part by the canopy of foliage overhead, was, of all the seemingly available places, regularly chosen for its perch by a little yellow-bellied Flycatcher. That twig must have met most nearly the specifications instinctively prescribed by the bird as a vantage-point whence it could sally out in customary fashion for passing insects. This strategic perch is now gone.

My corner tree used to have knotholes. Naturally, when a dead branch breaks off, or even is simply sawed off, decay starts in along the fiber and, proceeding faster than the surrounding bark can heal over the wound, leads to the formation of an open cavity. One such cavity, years ago, furnished the home site for a Screech Owl, and from it each summer issued a brood of young owls. Another knothole, of similar history but lesser dimensions, furnished the nesting place in spring, and the roosting place at all seasons, of a mutually devoted pair of Titmouses. Nowadays, it seems, the tenets of tree surgery require that no such cavities be permitted to remain in any well-cared-for tree. Each and every former and even potential knothole has been gouged out and sealed up, so that only a forbidding wall of cement meets the eye and beak of any prospecting bird.

Each year, when the campus oaks spring into green leaf, there appears a generation of little green worms. Some years these are few in number, in other years many—so many that the first crop of the green leaves upon which they feed may be conspicuously thinned out. With the appearance of the worms, numerous birds assemble in the leafage, to profit by the food supply newly afforded. The permanently resident kinds of birds are joined at that season by troops of migrating Warblers. These natural checks to the perfectly natural worm crop, must not, however, have been noted by the 'landscape architect'; for the spraying apparatus goes, of recent springs, from tree to tree—and Faculty Glade becomes quickly silent of warbler voices.

Year by year, in fine, I note the withdrawal from the campus proper of one after another of the more specialized types of birds, not only those that live in trees but also those that find a livelihood in normally growing shrubbery. This local disappearance of our native bird-life, a delight to the eye and ear of him who sees and hears, parallels significantly the establishment of *formality*—the removal of the elements of naturalness—in our campus flora.

What constitutes attractiveness in human environment all depends upon one's individual point of view.

Presence and Absence of Animals

A CERTAIN KIND of bird, the California Sage Sparrow, exists in numbers on the dry plains of the upper San Joaquin Valley, but not one has been found on the dry plains of the upper Sacramento Valley. A certain kind of mammal, the Red-bellied Harvest Mouse, exists abundantly in the salt marshes of the south arm of San Francisco Bay; but it has never been known to occur on the salt marshes of the north side of this bay or on those of Monterey Bay or of Humboldt Bay. Speaking now and henceforth of the higher vertebrate animals (mammals, birds, reptiles, and amphibians), I know of no kind of animal found within the boundaries of the State of California that exists, or within humanly historical times has existed, over the entire area of the State. In making this statement I have taken into account even the species of largest size, like mountain lions and grizzly bears, as well as those of the greatest powers of locomotion, like swallows and certain bats. It is true that some kinds of animals exist beyond the boundaries of California, to the north of us, *or to the south of us, or,* a few of them, in both of these directions. But all of these are de-limited in their occurrence more or less short of our eastern boundary; they do not reach into Nevada. There are in California a number of *other* species that *do* extend eastward into Nevada, from middle or southern California, but these either do not extend beyond, or even to, the *northern* boundary of our State, *or* they fail to reach to the *Mexican* border. In formulating these statements 1,149 vertebrate species and subspecies were considered, comprising 427 of mammals, 602 of birds, 83 of reptiles, and 37 of amphibians. Stating the case broadly and generally, it may be said: There is no species of vertebrate animal that exists everywhere in California; every species is restricted in its occurrence more or less short of the entire area of the State.

Let us see if this observed phenomenon, of presence and absence of animals, be vested with worthy significance.

I am going at this discussion of animal distribution at what I consider to be the bottom of the question, by dealing with the ranges of smallest compass, with the problems of most local situation. It seems to me just as inadequate to study the significance of distribution on the basis primarily of the areas of high distributional rank (world realms, regions, and the like), as to deal with the evolution of the animals themselves only or chiefly from a consideration of the higher systematic groups (phyla, classes, orders, and families); the thing to do is to deal with the component units, the areas of smallest extent occupied by the species and subspecies.

Furthermore, processes which it is possible to recognize right here and now are, I think likely, to be quite what they ever were anywhere and everywhere, at least since the outset of vertebrate phylogeny. The first stages in the separation of populations are before us right now, to be observed, together with the conditions permitting, indeed, forcing them—the same sort of beginnings as have occurred in remotely past times and have led, with the lapse of time, to momentous results.

One factor in the problem—and one that must be kept in view from the outset—concerns rate of reproduction. This follows the well-known geometric ratio by which proliferation of individuals leads to a drastic pressure for survival within the territory of the species—the severest sort of intracompetition. The outcome of this life-and-death struggle among the individuals leads inevitably, conditions governing their existence permitting, to quasi relief through emigration.

If this internal expansive force making for the spread of populations were exerted without restriction the outline of the geographic range of any given species as registered on a map would be a perfect circle; but in working out the ranges of animals we have never found any case of a range with so symmetrical an outline. On the contrary, mapped areas of occurrence of animals are, as a rule, extremely irregular in outline, and this very irregularity is significant of the critical nature, or inexorableness, of the conditions which act varyingly in different directions to delimit these ranges.

As I stated at the outset, nearer or farther away in all directions from its approximate center of occurrence, every species is absolutely stopped. What are termed barriers to distribution sooner or later intervene. These barriers are, in each case, comprised in the limits of the set of conditions which provide adequate means of subsistence for the particular species and which that species can tolerate. Beyond those limits some factor or condition essential for the existence of the species is wanting, or there is present in the environment some factor which the species cannot tolerate. What is the nature of the more common of these barriers?

The most obvious barrier limiting the distribution of higher vertebrate animals is some sort of physical or mechanical obstruction. Such an obstruction affects directly the individuals of the species that encounter it, either by stopping their advance or by destroying outright those that attempt to cross it. Land is a barrier of this sort to aquatic animals; channels or bodies of water constitute a similar barrier to purely terrestrial animals.

For example, the larger lowland streams of the San Joaquin-Sacramento basin together comprise, or have comprised within historical times, the entire habitat of the semi-aquatic Golden Beaver, a race of beaver peculiar to this territory and whose range stopped short of the heads of the tributary streams. In the case of this beaver the effective barrier to its farther spreading on the north, east, and south was the surrounding upland untraversed by any waterway; westwardly, the ocean barred its way.

The Golden Gate together with San Francisco Bay and the Strait of Carquinez constitutes an impassable barrier at the south for a certain species of chaparral-inhabiting chipmunk which exists in Marin and Sonoma counties. Toward the north that same waterway is the barrier which delimits the range of the California Ground Squirrel, so common on the slopes of the Berkeley hills. Very many similar cases of physical limitation may easily be cited from the near neighborhood of Berkeley.

Of the vertebrates within the entire State of California, however, by far the greater number of species find their geographic limitations without any direct reference to land or water boundaries. In other words, their ranges fall more or less short of tracts of waterless land or of coast lines or river banks. The barriers here concerned are intangible, but they must nevertheless be powerful, since by their action the spreading of species, of genera, and even of families is held in check quite as surely as by some tangible obstruction.

Furthermore, to the individual animal these invisible barriers may be no check at all, as is illustrated by kinds capable of free locomotion—volant ones; but the *species is* affected. The Mockingbird in its California distribution is closely confined to those parts of the State possessing orchard-like stands of small trees and certain climatic features, among them long and warm summers; but vagrant Mockingbirds, chiefly in autumn and early winter and only for a portion of the year, are found to occur far beyond the limits of these critically favorable conditions, to the westward and even to the northward of the breeding territory. What may become of such pioneers, whether they find their way back, or perish, is, in the case of the Mockingbird, not known.

Carnivorous mammals, such as bears and foxes, are well known to be subject to sporadic strayings on the part of individuals; but the *species* remain within set bounds, kept there by some effective though invisible set of factors. The very fact that individuals seem quite capable of transgressing these bounds, and yet that the mass of the population is not able permanently to overstep them, emphasizes all the more the remarkable potency of these barriers. Mountain ranges, by the way, are rarely hindrances at all, per se, but only as they involve other sorts of barriers, such as those of climate and vegetation.

Briefly, our study of these sets of facts concerning what may be called comparative distribution, together with observations upon the natural history of the animals, leads us to designate among the intangible kinds of barriers the following: (1) increase or decrease in prevailing temperature beyond certain critical points, these points, however, varying with different species; (2) increase or decrease in prevailing humidity of the air beyond certain limits, these limits again varying greatly, according to the species; (3) local modifications in available food supply beyond that which, in sort and amount, is sufficient to support a given animal of certain specialized ability to make use of it; (4) the limits of a territory affording places suitable for use of a given species, as dens or nests for the young, whether unmodified or utilized as bases of construction, in accordance with the breeding instincts of the species; (5) the limits of a territory providing safe places or refuges which can be made of daily use, "as is" or modified, for resting or loafing on the part of the adult individuals of the species. For, be it known, daily rest is a necessity to all the higher animals that have been watched with this point in view.

With these last three conditions it is clearly apparent that the inherent, relatively fixed, structural characters of the species, *in conjunction with* the critical factors of the environment, prescribe the spatial limitations of each and every vertebrate animal.

Hans Gadow wrote a book entitled *The Wanderings of Animals*. I object to this title, as I also object to some of the ideas in the text of the book. Animal species do not wander about here and there, as if they followed passing whims. Rather, they remove through space with lapse of time only as they are *forced* to do so. Animal populations, like individuals, are naturally inert. They "stay put" closely unless and until force from within or without comes to act upon them, and they then respond only to the extent that they *must*.

Animal species emigrate, along lines of least environmental resistance, only as they are compelled to do so, and as they *are directed,* by changing conditions. And this is a continuous and relatively rapid process of compulsion, speaking even in common chronological terms. The geological sciences tell us that land and water barriers, and barriers of climate, are continually moving about over the earth's surface, because of uplift and depression, shiftings in atmospheric currents, and a variety of other causes. Animal populations are by these shifting barriers, as it were, *herded about*. The encroaching barrier on one side of an animal's territory of occupancy impinges against the population on that side. The strain may tend to be relieved on the opposite side, if the barrier on that side undergoes parallel shifting, with the result that the species as a whole may, down through a period of time, move in a set direction. Probably no animal is permitted to remain long in one place. Every animal in the existing fauna of a given area has been crowded in from somewhere else; each species may have had its own separate history as to date and route of arrival, or else, as in the cases of dependencies, species may have come in groups. If it should happen that a barrier impinge on one side of the range of a species without corresponding retreat of the barrier on the other side, the habitat available to the species would be reduced like the space between the jaws of a parallel pliers; it might, indeed, finally disappear: the species would have become extinct.

The movements of species spatially are therefore not in the nature of "wanderings," but are manifestations of a most drastic process involving death continually not only to hordes of individuals but to numbers of subspecies and species, and even now and then involving the disappearance of higher systematic groups. Extinction is an inevitable accompaniment of the continual shifting and disappearing of environments. There is compensation, it is true, in the evolution of new forms—subspecies, then species and higher groups, as conditioned and guided by precedent and accompanying differentiation of habitats. But that is another though obviously closely associated theme.

In studying these matters, I have come to use the term "ecologic niche." This expression is intended to stand for the concept of the ultimate distributional unit, within which each species is held by its structural and instinctive limitations, these being subject only to exceedingly slow modification down through time. To illustrate from examples close at hand:

Examination, from one end of California to the other, of the localities where Pocket Gophers thrive, as compared with territory where these rodents do not occur, shows clearly close concordance of presence with certain special conditions: food of a sort usable in accord with the inherent equipment of this subterraneous animal to gather and digest it—roots, tubers, and underground stems of plants; a consistency of soil which, in accord with the animal's inherent propensity and equipment for digging, makes possible the driving of tunnels in order to reach this food and also to secure safety from enemies. Locally as well, the occurrence of gophers about the Berkeley hills is seen to concord with these two critical factors. The ecologic niche of this animal is therefore comprised within the terrain that provides these special features of environment.

Another example is the Meadow-lark. This species makes use of a rather wide range of plant and animal foods, but the bird is equipped to get its food safely and in adequate amount only from ground surface which is open—clothed with a low type of plant cover. For successful food-getting, therefore, and for escape from its enemies, the bird is specialized for existence upon a meadow or grassy plain. Its range locally is sharply de-limited in most directions at the margins of the meadow type of habitat, as where the meadow is interrupted by forest, brush land, marsh, rock surface, or sand flat. Furthermore, within this general associational habitat, close observation shows that for its nest the Meadow-lark employs only certain types of meadow-land cover and that it chooses for its food chiefly items of a certain relatively large caliber. Other birds living in the same meadow association levy their toll upon other sources of subsistence afforded there. These different species are able compatibly to occupy the same habitat because no two of them depend upon precisely the same means of subsistence. Thus the ultimate unit in the general association occupied by each single species, Meadow-lark or any other bird, is its ecologic niche.

No two species in the same general territory can occupy for long identically the same ecologic niche. If, by chance, the vagaries of distributional movement result in introducing into a new territory the ecologic homologue of a species already endemic in that territory, competitive displacement of one of the species by the other is bound to take place. Perfect balance is inconceivable. An instance is afforded by the European Starling recently introduced into the eastern states where it is displacing certain native species of birds. The Chinese Starling, or Mynah, is behaving similarly in British Columbia in northwestern America; and there is the classic case of the English Sparrow.

Recognition of the ecologic niche may follow a method analogous to that employed in systematic synthesis. Somewhat as systematists may profitably and significantly group subspecies into species, species into genera, genera into families, families into orders, orders into classes, and classes into phyla—so may students of distribution build from the bottom, by appropriate handling of habitats. Ecologic niches may be considered in groups comprising associations; associations may be grouped into faunal areas; faunal areas may usefully be considered in series called life-zones, which subdivide continents; and life-zones may be grouped into regions, and these into world realms.

I will now attempt to picture initial stages in the process of the spreading of animals that are illustrated close at hand and may therefore be verified, I believe, by any patient local observer. This picture presupposes the recognition of the inherent habits of an animal, its instincts, no less essentially than the obvious features in its anatomical structure. The picture is based upon observational natural history—quite as worthy a route of obtaining knowledge, when suitably disciplined, as laboratory experimentation, and a method which alone is practicable for obtaining information of this kind. The wild mammal on the University campus that we know best is the California, or Digger, Ground Squirrel. Some of us field naturalists have been watching this animal season after season now for eighteen years. Its particular habitat, its ecologic niche, distinctive among those of the twenty-nine other native kinds of mammals of our neighborhood, may be characterized as follows: open ground, not woods or chaparral; grass-land, whether hilltop, slope, or on a level; ground that is fairly safe from inundation when rain falls heavily; ground that the animal, with rather limited powers of excavation, can dig into sufficiently far for the establishment of safety refuges and breeding dens; presence of a type of vegetation which produces an abundant annual crop of seeds or grain.

As to numbers, the most favorable parts of the upper campus possess a maximum population at the beginning of the breeding season of twenty ground squirrels per acre. Censuses taken in the fall, at the close of the breeding season, by members of the class in Economic Vertebrate Zoology (Zoology 116), indicated a maximum number of sixty squirrels per acre near the old rifle range. There is fluctuation in size of population from year to year, apparently brought about chiefly by varying food supply, this in turn being influenced by amount and seasonal distribution of rainfall, as also by closeness of grazing by the competitory cattle.

As with other animals, the breeding season of this species is fixed seemingly so that the young will be launched into the world in the early part of the season of plenty, which, for a spermophilous animal in the climate of west-central California, is comprised in the period from May to September. The young are born about April 1. There is one litter per year. The litter consists of from four to eleven young. Over 10,000 records of embryos, gathered by the United States Public Health Service, indicate an average of 7.2 young per litter. The proportion of the sexes in the adult population, as determined from the records of thousands of squirrels captured, is approximately fifty-fifty. We can therefore figure the breeding rate, even when eliminating 1.2 to be conservative, as three-fold annually. Two ground squirrels in March become eight ground squirrels by May—a 300 per cent increase.

The potentiality for increase on this basis is enormous. Fig-
uring the lifetime of a squirrel as five years, as is known for
some individuals, one pair of squirrels could theoretically give
origin in five years, while the initial pair is yet alive, to a population of 1,792. The normal population on the upper campus
of one acre could, theoretically, in five years produce a number
of squirrels sufficient to populate to the same density 896 acres,
or nearly one and one-half square miles. This rate of reproduction, characteristic of this species, provides it with a *power to
spread,* annually reinforced—to occupy territory to the limit
that territory of the right sort, appropriate to the species, is accessible to it.

This potential power to spread varies with different animals,
apparently in proportion to the varying vicissitudes of existence normally to be expected; it is to be measured by rate
of reproduction—50 per cent per annum in the slower breeding kinds, such as Antelope and Albatrosses, up to 600 per cent
in Quail and even 40,000 per cent per annum in the Common
Rat. Furthermore, the initial reproductive rate of a species is
a deep-seated character; it manifests itself from generation to
generation just as surely, and with as little variation, as a rule,
as a structural feature of the skull or of a tooth. Viability of
the young, however, is a factor that does vary greatly, prenatally
as well as postnatally, in accordance with amount of nourish-
ment, safety of breeding dens, etc.

When the young Digger Ground Squirrels are first born, in
the warm and dry, grass-lined underground den, the mother
cares for and nourishes them with the greatest solicitude. The
young grow rapidly and soon begin to develop a marked measure of aggressiveness. This shortly influences them to venture
forth from the entrances of the burrows. By the time a young-
ster, in ascertained cases, has reached only one-fourth the
weight of its mother, it is already venturing yards and even
rods away from its safety refuge.

By this stage and thenceforth, the mother herself shows less
and less concern for the welfare of her young; and by the time

the young are three-fourths grown the maternal instinct has disappeared and may show itself to be absolutely reversed. The young are no longer welcomed back into the parental burrow; clear evidences of intolerance become manifest. Simultaneously there appears on the part of the young a further increased degree of independence, of venturesomeness. What happens on the upper campus, literally as well as figuratively, is that along in July and August many of the young squirrels "go west." The 300 per cent ratio of multiplication has brought about a congestion of population there. The season of plenteous food-supply is passing. Individual competition ensues, not only as between young and adult but as between young and young. If by chance an adult has been killed, its territory is available for occupancy and, indeed, is promptly claimed by the most aggressive or most fortunate young one within reach of it. But the great majority of the young must establish precincts of their own, and to do so they start out individually to find new territory, buffeted hither and thither, with general trend of motion along lines of least resistance. The movement of individuals will naturally be away from centers of population toward sparsely populated ground. A late-summer emigration of individuals away from their natal territories becomes manifest. We see young-of-the-year making their appearance all along the eastern suburbs of Berkeley. Some of the more venturesome individuals, the more lucky ones with respect to continually waylaying dangers, both animate and inanimate, reach vacant lots right in town. This fall, individual squirrels, young-of-the-year, were seen in the vicinity of Hilgard Hall, on a lot at Dana and Allston, and on another lot at the corner of Euclid and Cedar.

In this process of dissemination there is an enormous sacrifice of individuals in the interest of the *species,* whereby the latter tries out in all directions for new territory to occupy—a primal law in the persistence of species. Granting that the population from year to year on an average holds just its own, then three times the number of squirrels that are in existence in

April inevitably perish in normal course within the succeeding twelve months. The limits of population in a territory of given fixed area are determined by the limits of the means of subsistence afforded by that area to the species in question. The annual mortality reflects the birth rate.

The ratio of reproduction inherent in a given species is observed to be far in excess of apparent real need. There is here a factor of safety in numbers to insure against the extermination of the species in event of extreme emergency. In the case of the California Ground Squirrel in the East Bay region a cause of mortality has come into the experience of the species doubtless absolutely new in its long-time history. I refer to the concentrated campaign against it by man, through the use of poisons, gassing, shooting, and trapping, because of the agency of the animal as a carrier of the dreaded bubonic, sometimes pneumonic, plague. In certain years, this campaign, covering the entire upper campus along with contiguous territory, has been waged with great vigor; not a year has gone by in the past eighteen, I believe, that some work has not been done against the squirrels. Yet the year of 1927 witnessed a seemingly quite normal population of ground squirrels on the area that happens to have been under our observation. They have come back again and again; and not only that, but numbers have been supplied sufficient to make conspicuous the process of post-breeding emigration just outlined.

In this process, again, vast numbers of the adventurous, vigorous young-of-the-year are inevitably destroyed each year by natural agencies; the western portion of the centrifugal movement has, in reality, all been to no avail. San Francisco Bay, impassable to a non-aquatic animal, is the ultimate barrier, and short of that the humanly populated coastal plain offers no opportunity of new establishment. Nevertheless there was the *chance*, well worth taking on the basis of long-time racial history, insured to the species by its great multiplication rate in conjunction with the complex of habits above described.

Much the same mechanism is observed far and wide among

other animals. The past year we have had mouse plagues—the results of favoring circumstances locally, involving adequate rainfall and consequent abundant food supply and shelter, together with previously reduced or failing natural checks. Bears and deer in the Yosemite manifest the same phenomenon, but by reason of their superior locomotivity are better able than ground squirrels to pioneer for new territory. They do so, however, with much the same results as the ground squirrels.

Birds, because of ease of movement, individually, from place to place, are far better off for pioneering than most mammals. They are at the opposite extreme from the pocket gopher and mole, our most sedentary mammals. Great numbers of scouts, we may call them, are sent off into surrounding territory from the metropolis of the avian species each autumn. This movement of individuals is not to be confused with the regular annual migratory movements of some species in which the entire mass of the population takes part.

In the case of birds, there is to be seen a perfection of process involving less sacrifice of individuals than in the case of rodents. A lesser rate of reproduction is required. In birds, we see the operation of a more refined *preference* on the part of the individual—by virtue of which each scout is able, wherever it finds itself, to look about, move freely, and *choose* surroundings consistent with the peculiar structural needs of its species, for food, for shelter, and for safe breeding places. The Song Sparrow taking part in the post-breeding dissemination (and such is apparently always, judging from specimens collected, a young-of-the-year, just as with the ground squirrel) does not blindly content itself with an attempt to find subsistence on grassy upland, or in a forest, or in dry chaparral, but keeps going, seeks out locally its own "natural" type of habitat, the stream-side thicket—the ecologic niche of its species. By the exercise of choice in the selection of habitat, a great saving of individuals is accomplished; and this involves, of course, a character in the cerebral equipment of the species which, like each external peculiarity in its structure, is itself, in partial measure at least, the result of a protracted pressure upon the organism from the complex of environmental factors to which the race has been subject down through time.

To repeat, the bird species, of superior locomotivity and by reason of its possession of highly developed ability to choose, is able to try out new territory on the periphery of its habitat with greater chances for success, and this is done year after year and generation after generation, giving maximum powers of accommodation to habitats which are enlarging, to habitats which are shifting spatially, to habitats which are recurring at more or less remote points from their main precedent locations, to new types of habitats which are gradually evolving.

Barriers to distribution which are effective in absolute degree are really in small minority. We think of the ocean as an absolute barrier to terrestrial species. It *is* so, to mammals such as the ground squirrel, pocket gopher, and mole; but individuals of volant and swimming kinds reach across broad channels to more or less remote islands and now and then succeed in establishing new colonies of their species there. And natural vegetational rafts are believed by some students, now and then, by chance, to ferry passengers from one land mass to another.

At this point, the reader may properly ask as to the nature of the *evidence* upon which sound distributional studies are to be made. How can we say with confidence concerning a given species whether it is or is not present in a given territory?

Certain species of higher vertebrates are characterized conspicuously on the basis of size or of prominent external features. In the case of the Antelope and the Elk, for example, it is fairly safe to accept common human testimony as to presence, back quite to the beginnings of western history. The same is true of such a bird as the Sage Grouse or the Valley Quail. But, curiously, no such degree of dependence can be placed upon common report of the Grizzly Bear. The distinctions between the Grizzly and the brown phase of the American Black Bear are not commonly known. Confusion of these distinct kinds of bears has been, indeed, common among even experienced sportsmen and hunters. Here, then, rigid discrimination in accepting evidence must be exercised by the distributionist or else wrong inferences will be drawn.

As a matter of fact, with the great majority of the species of birds and mammals, of reptiles and amphibians, there is only one acceptable basis for determining presence and that is the taking of actual specimens and the preservation of these permanently, with attached, signed statements of locality and other circumstances of capture. So-called "sight records," even of the commonest birds, have proved over and over again to be wrong. Many, many species and subspecies are difficult enough of systematic determination with actual specimens in hand; especially is this true as regards the ultimate taxonomic unit, of greatest significance, the subspecies. The results of distributional study to be valid must be made on the basis of accurate identifications of materials; and these materials must be preserved so as to permit of repeated verification as refinements in systematic analysis accompany increased experience. Hence the research museum, functioning as the repository for this accumulating evidence. Popular testimony, impression, the sight record, have, perhaps, their place in the "romance" of natural history; but this province belongs to literature and not to science.

It is highly probable that at the present time barriers to animal distribution are changing in position and effectiveness more rapidly than at any other time in the world's history. An entirely new factor, man, with his machinery and ever increasing aggressiveness, is removing or rendering permeable the barriers which heretofore have hemmed in animal species. He has been an agent causing the advancement of some barriers, the retreat of others, the weakening of many; and in nearly every direction we can see examples of his effacement of ecologic niches altogether, with the resulting quick extinction of their occupants.

With the cutting of timber and clearing of the land in California's coast belt north of San Francisco Bay the Coyote, a plains animal, has, within the memory of men now living, extended its range westward almost or quite to the seacoast. With the same process, of timber-cutting and clearing of the land, forest-inhabiting species of birds and mammals have been compelled to retreat, notably two species of game birds, the Sooty Dusky Grouse and the Oregon Ruffed Grouse.

Still nearer home, indeed right here on the upper campus, and within the compass of but eighteen years, we have witnessed conspicuous fluctuations in bird populations. Certain hilltops which I have in mind, situated between the Big "C" and Grizzly Peak, were originally bald, clothed chiefly with grass or else a low scattered type of chaparral, in which the California sage was a dominant element. On those areas, eighteen years ago, the characteristic birds were Meadow-larks, Horned Larks, Burrowing Owls, Rufous-crowned Sparrows, and, in winter, Pipits, Savannah Sparrows, and other meadow-land types from the north.

Then man, on the theory that a timber cover would in some way increase the water supply from the hills, proceeded to plant non-native trees thickly over this territory that we have in mind. These trees grew rapidly and thrived for a time; a young forest appeared, and the birds just named disappeared. Some individuals, perhaps, moved elsewhere; but, strictly speaking, the total meadow-land territory, for these species essential to their existence, was restricted by just so much: the total population of the species was reduced by just the number of individuals that the area thus newly forested had originally supported.

Now the newly rising forest introduced a new avian environment. Scouts, pioneers, from populations occupying the same associations at greater or less distance found themselves, through post-breeding dissemination, in this newly arising and favorable habitat and established themselves there. From about 1915 to 1923 we found on those hilltop acres a new assembly of birds, lovers of open forest, consisting of Western Lark Sparrows, Western Chipping Sparrows, Lawrence Goldfinches,

Juncos, Mourning Doves in summer, and others—each of these species finding within the general association its own separate ultimate ecologic niche, and thus living compatibly with its close associates.

Then came beetles and fungi and other enemies of the pines —and fire, against which even the eucalyptus could not stand. The young forest was killed and the skeletons of the trees littered the territory. The second category of birds disappeared, and a further stage in this natural experiment ensued. A third group of birds discovered it—consisting of those kinds which find subsistence on or in dead and decaying wood. Last year, Hairy and Downy Woodpeckers were present, certain Wrens put in their appearance, Flickers made nesting cavities in the rotting tree-trunks, and in deserted ones of these cavities, Western Bluebirds and Sparrow Hawks had by April selected their nesting places. This is the phase of bird occupation now observable on that territory. What is next in order? Probably disappearance of all vestiges of the trees and a return to original bald hilltop condition. Woodpeckers and Wrens and Bluebirds will vanish and once again the Meadow-lark, Horned Lark, Rufous-crowned Sparrow, and Burrowing Owl will come into their own—by re-discovery on the part of pioneers, of the territory then newly available for occupancy.

Eternal fluctuation of this sort is a law of the Earth; but man and his devices are speeding up its action to a rate probably never before reached in the world's history.

A further illustration: A species of water bird, the California Clapper Rail, is endemic in the salt marshes of the San Francisco Bay region. It is adapted to use for its food the invertebrate life of the mud-bottomed tidal sloughs. The marsh vegetation (pickleweed, salt grass, and grindelia) provide it with cover, for safety and for nesting places. A recent detailed survey by Dudley De Groot shows that the territory occupied by the Clapper Rail has through man's encroachment been reduced to but a fraction of its original extent. Salt ponds, flying fields, reclamation of lands by diking and draining, for agriculture, for factory sites, and for living quarters, are impinging year by year more and more upon the Bay marshes. On Bay Farm Island, until ten years ago a metropolis of the rail on the east side of the Bay, not a rail is now to be seen; and this statement applies also, with probably equal pertinence, to a number of associated species of native birds and mammals.

It is probable that "Californians Incorporated," a commercial agency whose efforts are expended vigorously toward securing congestion of human population in the San Francisco Bay region, is right now the greatest single enemy of wild animal life in west-central California. The slogan "where life is better" is a curious perversion: it has sinister portents for even man himself.

An act of man is now pending which will affect the Colorado River on the southeastern boundary of California. A huge retaining dam will serve to "regulate" the flow of water below it. In the season of low water, without any doubt whatsoever in extra dry years, not a rill of water will be flowing down the main channel of the Colorado River, at least in portions of its lower course.

Now the Colorado River is an ancient stream; it has an aquatic fauna peculiarly its own, including peculiar races of such conspicuous mammals as beaver, otter, and muskrat. Persistence of these animals is threatened. With the effacement of their habitats their fate is sealed. Furthermore, the Colorado River until now has been an impassable barrier to many of the characteristic animals of the desert territory which this river has from time immemorial traversed. With the withdrawal of the water from its channel there will be dry land from bank to bank, and desert animals from the one side can and will cross over to the other unhindered. The river barrier to them will have disappeared. Desert tortoises, heretofore known only from the California side of the river, will have free access to Arizona territory. The Gila Monsters of Arizona, heretofore strictly limited to the territory east of the Colorado River, will, in a long-time sense, pour over into California; and so on with at least sixteen other species of terrestrial vertebrates.

An old law of animal geography may be re-worded and amplified as follows: A given kind of animal native in one place is also to be found living somewhere else (1) except as it has been unable to cross an intervening barrier; (2) except as, having crossed the barrier, it has not found the ecologic niche to which it is inherently adapted; (3) except as it has found its own ecologic niche across the barrier to be already occupied fully and exclusively; (4) except as, in this new and appropriate habitat across the barrier, having gained initial foothold it has failed, after fair trial, because of inferior adaptational equipment, altogether to replace its ecologic competitor or homologue.

Man, as regards his own *individuals*, has overcome all barriers to distribution over the earth's surface, though barriers effective racially, involving mass of population, still exist for him, in one barrier at least, that of climate. And man's achievements in crossing natural barriers, individually, have and continue increasingly, incidentally, accidentally, or purposefully to include other animal life as well. In effect, man is building "bridges," in the distributional sense, for other animals across all sorts of barriers. Wherever man goes, by train or by ship, by auto or by airplane, animals do or can go with him. An African lion by airplane is the latest instance! Man's curiosity, his constant efforts to transplant animals seemingly valuable to him from place to place over the world's surface, his carelessness in permitting passengers unbidden to accompany him, warrant, I think, the suggestion that through his agency every animal species in the world bids fair to make its appearance, sooner or later as individuals, and each usually with a complement of "guests" or parasites, everywhere else. That is to say, barriers to individuals of vertebrate species, and many invertebrates as well, will have vanished. The problem of persistence henceforth will be dependent upon ecologic factors: upon whether or not the introduced or transplanted stock of a given animal can survive after having got into the new locality.

And there are portents, as well as present actualities, in all this process that bear inevitably upon man's own interests. The economics of animal distribution need to be heeded.

Only the other day I saw exhibited in a building on this campus some living Hamsters. They had come to America, convoyed by a young medical investigator across the Pacific for the purpose of experimentation. These animals, Hamsters, are very generalized, mouse-like rodents of the Orient and other portions of the Old World. They represent an aggressive, prodigiously prolific type of animal whose numbers are limited, apparently, chiefly if not solely by limit of food supply. As to shelter they are widely adaptable. According to Lydekker, from six to eighteen young comprise a single litter; and two litters are borne by a female in one year. The species feeds upon grain and is a ravager of crops. One can conceive of some accident by which a family of Hamsters would find themselves at large in our country, with devastation in prospect similar to that which did happen in the case of the rabbits introduced into Australia.

We have in America, already established, an Old World rodent, the Common or Brown Rat, which has been designated by Dr. E. W. Nelson, of the United States Department of Agriculture, as not only the most destructive vertebrate animal in America to property, but the most dangerous one to human life in the whole world because of its disease-carrying agency.

It is true that we have established quarantine regulations. But I observe that these regulations are applied for the most part only against animals already proved to be injurious. For example, there is stringent law against the introduction of the European Starling, the Chinese Starling, and the English Sparrow. But each of these birds is already established in North America beyond recall. There is no regulation that I am aware of against the importation of Hamsters!

An ever recurring menace, I am confident, is involved in the efforts of sportsmen to bring into California alien game species. The Chinese or Ring-necked Pheasant and the Hungarian Partridge are instances of this purposeful transplantation of animals far beyond their naturally limiting barriers. The introduction, successfully from the standpoint of those who did it, of the Oriental *carp* ruined our native lowland fish fauna.

Let us set aside the economic phase of our problem at this point and return to the purely theoretical one. Inductions from observations such as I have last cited point toward a possible law, originally suggested to me by the mammalogist Seton, which may be stated as follows.

When a species native to a large area, such as a continental land mass, is introduced into a new smaller area (which, of course, must provide the ecologic niche appropriate for that species), then the species which is native in this smaller area, occupying the same ecologic niche, and with which the introduced species comes into competition, is soon supplanted. In other words, the invader from a large territory usually, if it becomes established at all, does so by competitively replacing a species native in the smaller area. A score of cases support this law, to one that illustrates a possible opposite course of events. I can refer to numerous European vertebrates introduced into Australia and New Zealand, to Australian species introduced into New Zealand, and to Oriental and European (that is, Eurasian) species introduced into North America.

It looks to me as though the environment of large compass, where the long-time inhabitants have been subjected to the widest range in the rigors of existence, has developed species, through drastic processes of trial and discard, of the greatest degree of hardihood; and correlated with, or a phase of, this hardihood is an innate aggressiveness as manifested by individuals as well as by whole populations.

The European House Sparrow, the European Starling, and the Chinese Mynah, endemically Eurasian birds, have been spreading since their introduction into North America at an amazing rate. Testimony overwhelmingly is to the effect that native American species of wild birds are giving way locally before these aliens. The ultimate result in a number of cases, as witnessed in Australia and New Zealand, is that the introduced species from the larger territory has crowded the native ones to the wall—led, in some cases, to their outright extinction. One is reminded of the process of displacement, now nearly complete, of the race *Homo sapiens americanus,* by the European *Homo sapiens sapiens.* The fate of a race is often sealed by the breaking down of the barrier that originally isolated it from a more adaptable or aggressive relative.

A visualization of the future, after this world-new process of barrier-bridging by man has been under way for a few centuries, is of a world with island faunas, and faunas of the lesser continents, wiped out, supplanted by sets of niche-occupants, ecologic homologues, from the largest land mass; a world of relatively *few* species established *widely* over the earth's surface.

Differentiation Areas

ANALYSIS of the mass of distributional data given in the main part of the present paper* leads to the recognition of a number of separate areas in Lower California each of which possesses species or subspecies, or both, peculiar to itself. In each area the differentiation of these characterizing species and subspecies (to be termed differentiates) appears to be directly correlated with certain conditions having to do with degree and duration of isolation of their populations during passed time together with environmental peculiarities involving climate, shelter, and food. But there has been marked irregularity of results in the several areas; and this circumstance, of varying effectiveness, would seem to provide opportunity for determining some of the factors involved. Before further discussion, I will designate the ten differentiation areas which seem to me discernible within the territory of Lower California and list the subspecies and species of land birds which appear to belong characterizingly to each.

1. Subspecies and species of land birds believed to have been differentiated within the CAPE DISTRICT of Lower California:

Lophortyx californica achrustera	Empidonax difficilis cineritius
Columba fasciata vioscae	Aphelocoma californica hypoleuca
Falco sparverius peninsularis	Icterus cucullatus trochiloides
Otus asio xantusi	Carpodacus mexicanus ruberrimus
Bubo virginianus elachistus	Junco bairdi
Glaucidium gnoma hoskinsii	Amphispiza bilineata bangsi
Micropallas whitneyi sanfordi	Aimophila ruficeps sororia
Crotophaga sulcirostris pallidula	Pipilo maculatus magnirostris
Dryobates scalaris lucasanus	Pipilo fuscus albigula
Balanosphyra formicivora angustifrons	Richmondena cardinalis ignea
Centurus uropygialis brewsteri	Pyrrhuloxia sinuata peninsulae
Colaptes chrysoïdes chrysoïdes	Passerina versicolor pulchra
Phalaenoptilus nuttallii dickeyi	Progne subis hesperia
Chordeiles acutipennis inferior	Tachycineta thalassina brachyptera
Basilinna xantusii	Lanius ludovicianus nelsoni
Myiarchus cinerascens pertinax	Vireo solitarius lucasanus
Sayornis nigricans brunnescens	Vireo huttoni cognatus
Myiochanes richardsonii peninsulae	Dendroica erithachorides castaneiceps

* A Distributional Summation of the Ornithology of Lower California.

[1. Subspecies and species of land birds believed to have been differentiated within the Cape District of Lower California—*Continued*]

Geothlypis beldingi beldingi
Toxostoma cinereum cinereum
Heleodytes brunneicapillus affinis
Sitta carolinensis lagunae
Baeolophus inornatus cineraceus

Psaltriparus minimus grindae
Auriparus flaviceps lamprocephalus
Polioptila caerulea obscura
Polioptila melanura abbreviata
Turdus confinis

2. Subspecies believed to have been differentiated within the San Pedro Mártir District (including the so-called San Quintín District):

Oreortyx picta confinis
Lophortyx californica plumbea
Dryobates villosus scrippsae
Dryobates scalaris eremicus
Balanosphyra formicivora martirensis
Centurus uropygialis cardonensis
Colaptes cafer martirensis
Colaptes chrysoïdes brunnescens
Sayornis saya quiescens
Sayornis nigricans salictaria
Aphelocoma californica obscura
Junco oreganus townsendi
Aimophila ruficeps lambi
Pipilo maculatus umbraticola

Pipilo fuscus senicula
Lanius ludovicianus grinnelli
Toxostoma cinereum mearnsi
Toxostoma crissale trinitatis
Heleodytes bruneicapillus bryanti
Thryomanes bewickii charienturus
Sitta carolinensis alexandrae
Sitta pygmaea leuconucha
Baeolophus inornatus murinus
Penthestes gambeli atratus
Psaltriparus minimus melanurus
Chamaea fasciata canicauda
Polioptila melanura californica
Sialia mexicana anabelae

3. Subspecies believed to have been differentiated within the San Ignacio District, in the lower waist of the peninsula:

Otocoris alpestris enertera
Passerculus rostratus halophilus
Amphispiza belli cinerea
Melospiza melodia rivularis
Pipilo fuscus aripolius

Geothlypis beldingi goldmani
Toxostoma lecontei arenicola
Thryomanes bewickii cerroensis
Polioptila melanura margaritae

4. Subspecies and species believed to have been differentiated within the Colorado Desert District, though some of them not necessarily or probably within the territory included within the northeastern boundaries of Lower California:

Lophortyx gambelii gambelii
Otus asio gilmani
Dryobates scalaris cactophilus
Centurus uropygialis uropygialis
Colaptes chrysoïdes mearnsi
Phalaenoptilus nuttallii hueyi
Otocoris alpestris leucansiptila
Agelaius phoeniceus sonoriensis

Passerculus rostratus rostratus
Melospiza melodia saltonis
Pipilo aberti
Piranga rubra cooperi
Dendroica aestiva sonorana
Toxostoma lecontei lecontei
Toxostoma crissale crissale
Polioptila melanura melanura

5. Subspecies believed to have been differentiated in the San Diegan District, altogether north of the United States boundary, but which extend a greater or less distance into Lower California, even as far in some cases as 30° latitude:

Otus asio quercinus
Otocoris alpestris actia
Agelaius phoeniceus neutralis
Aimophila ruficeps canescens

Melospiza melodia cooperi
Pipilo maculatus megalonyx
Pipilo fuscus crissalis
Geothlypis trichas scirpicola

6. Subspecies believed to have been differentiated within the Sierra Juárez District:

Junco oreganus pontilis

7. Subspecies and species believed to have been differentiated on Guadalupe Island:

Polyborus lutosus
Colaptes cafer rufipileus
Carpodacus amplus
Junco insularis

Pipilo consobrinus
Salpinctes obsoletus guadeloupensis
Thryomanes brevicauda
Corthylio calendula obscurus

8. Species and subspecies believed to have been differentiated on the San Benito Islands:

Carpodacus mcgregori   Passerculus rostratus guttatus

9. Subspecies believed to have been differentiated on Los Coronados Islands:

Melospiza melodia coronatorum

10. Subspecies which are believed to have been differentiated on the Santa Barbara Islands, hence entirely to the northwestward of the confines of Lower California, but whose ranges extend to include certain islands, or even the mainland, along the northwestern coast of the peninsula:

Carpodacus mexicanus clementis   Vermivora celata sordida

The bird life of the entire peninsula of Lower California, as long ago indicated by Merriam (1892) and Allen (1893), and as more recently demonstrated by Nelson (1921), is essentially of northern relationships rather than Mexican or Tropical. In other words, it may be said with confidence that the peninsula as a whole has been populated by more or less remote as well as recent invasions, by way of its basal territory, from California, Arizona, and Sonora.

A way to test this matter is to examine the differentiates which characterize the area farthest sequestered. This area is, of course, the Cape District. There are forty-six forms listed above as having originated in this area; and in all these cases but three the pioneer ancestors can most reasonably be thought of, in my opinion, as having arrived from the north, at one time or another, over continuous land, rather than from across the Gulf to the eastward.

These three exceptions in the Cape avifauna (*Crotophaga sulcirostris pallidula, Basilinna xantusii* and *Dendroica eri-*

thachorides castaneiceps) belong to the Tropical life-zone and were most probably originally established by vagrants from across the water. Furthermore, vagrants of probably southern route, which are known to have arrived in the peninsula (but which have not become established) are only two, namely, *Compsothlypis graysoni* and *Euthlypis lachrymosa tephra*. The numerous other recent vagrants recorded from Lower California can all be accounted for as coming in from the north; the process now is thus likely quite as it has been in the past, whenever not interrupted by mid-peninsular submergence.

There is no differentiate in any other area than the Cape District that is not of positively northern affinities (that is, Californian or Sonoran). Several other of the differentiates in the Cape District, in addition to the three named above, have, I am aware, been listed as "Tropical." These (notably *Micropallas whitneyi sanfordi, Richmondena cardinalis ignea, Pyrrhuloxia sinuata peninsulae,* and *Passerina versicolor pulchra*) could easily have come in over the Colorado Desert route, especially during cycles of unusually warm climate, becoming established then on permanent basis at the lower end of the peninsula where the climate at low altitudes has doubtless remained most continuously of Tropical warmth, favorable to the several species in question. To repeat the idea, 94 per cent of the differentiates in the Cape District were antecedently Boreal or Austral in origin, as were all the differentiates in the remaining nine districts of Lower California.

The area next most prolific of differentiates, the San Pedro Mártir District, including much of the northern, most elevated part of the peninsula, has twenty-eight forms peculiar to it. Most of these are races of Boreal or Upper Austral species— links in continuous series from the north, terminal races or else with further differentiates to the south, in the San Ignacio District or in the Cape District, or in both. (See, for example, the accompanying maps* for *Lophortyx, Junco, Aimophila, Pipilo, Lanius, Thryomanes, Sitta,* and *Baeolophus.*) In one

* Omitted.

case, *Toxostoma cinereum mearnsi,* I think we see the results of a secondary invasion, northward from the Cape District, of a species differentiated in the latter area from an ancestor still more precedently of Sonoran origin. The structural features of the series of thrashers within which *T. cinereum* lies, coupled with their distributional occurrence, indicate this.

The area I here call the San Ignacio District, using the term proposed by Bancroft (1926) but not with the same significance, is interlying and poorly developed as regards endemic differentiates. There are nine of them. Six are terminal in series from the north; two (*Pipilo fuscus aripolius* and *Polioptila melanura margaritae*) are intermediate steps between San Pedro Mártir and Cape forms of species continuously distributed up and down the peninsula; and one (*Geothlypis beldingi goldmani*) is of closest affinity with a Cape District differentiate.

Immediately to the north of the San Pedro Mártir District proper is a mountain mass showing, among birds, just one Boreal differentiate, *Junco oreganus pontilis.* Otherwise, this weakly marked differentiation center, the Juárez District, lies predominantly within the influence of the San Pedro Mártir District. It is to be observed here that my conception of the territory involved in the latter district extends to include the entire gamut of species, Austral as well as Boreal, which appear to have come under the peculiar "humid-desert" type of climate conditioned, seemingly, by the presence and position of the lofty San Pedro Mártir range. The lowlands west to the seacoast and even the nearby islands plainly fall within this climatic area.

At the northeast, in the potent Colorado Desert District, we find entering the territory of Lower California a number of Sonoran birds, some of them in far-differentiated form—full species, like *Pipilo aberti, Toxostoma lecontei,* and *Toxostoma crissale.* The latter two, and others, have evidently given origin secondarily (accompanying or following southward spreading of their populations) to near-related races in the San Pedro Mártir, the San Ignacio, and even the Cape District. Quite as interesting as the cases in which southward spreading and subsequent differentiation *has* occurred, are those cases in which the process has *not* taken place; for example, *Lophortyx gambelii.* The nature of the limiting barrier for this quail has not as yet been suggested.

At the northwest, influence upon the bird life of the adjacent portion of Lower California is seen to be exerted appreciably from the San Diegan District of southwestern Upper California. Eight essentially San Diegan differentiates, all of the Austral life-zone, penetrate more or less distance south, in four cases on the lower coastal strip clear through the San Pedro Mártir District (in its "San Quintín" section).

Insularity in passed time probably had a good deal to do in at least hastening the process of differentiation in the Cape District proper. At the present stage of land emergence or submergence none of the resulting islands possesses the area or the altitude or the wide range of ecologic conditions which doubtless pertained to the antecedent Cape District island. None of the existing islands shows, as regards birds, anywhere near the amount of racial difference that characterizes the Cape avifauna.

Guadalupe is the most remote of the many Lower Californian islands (for full descriptions of all these, see Nelson, 1921); it is of volcanic formation and was never connected with the mainland; it is of fair size (22 by 6 miles) and considerable altitude (up to 4500 feet); and it has, or originally had, a goodly number of diverse ecologic associations, including forest. All of its land birds must have reached it as vagrants, the eight differentiates in more or less remote times. Of the eight species thus represented, two (*Junco insularis* and *Corthylio calendula obscurus*) are Boreal, four (*Colaptes cafer rufipileus, Pipilo consobrinus, Salpinctes obsoletus guadeloupensis,* and *Thryomanes brevicauda*) may be considered essentially Upper Austral, and two (*Carpodacus amplus* and *Polyborus lutosus*) are likely Lower Austral, the last-named even Tropical, in zonal origin.

Despite its location 135 miles from the nearest mainland, Guadalupe Island, as seen from the evidence detailed in the present contribution, is receiving from year to year vagrant delegates from a wide range of mainland species. Only now and then do the ecologic conditions there, in coincidence with sufficient numbers of arriving vagrants of a given species, plus other critical factors of persistence, permit of colonial establishment. Such *has* occurred in the cases of *Loxia* and *Sitta*, though so recently as to have resulted in no appreciable degree of differentiation. In the genera represented by Guadalupe differentiates it is significant for their origin to recall the records, elsewhere specified, of waifs of *Salpinctes* and *Corthylio* on shipboard off the west coast of Lower California.

The San Benito group of islands is next to Guadalupe in importance for differentiation of birds. But the San Benitos are small, with few ecologic niches; and we find but two birds among the small number established upon them which are appreciably different from their congeners elsewhere. One of these (*Carpodacus mcgregori*) has been found also on the nearby Cedros Island, but whether or not as more than a vagrant there is not known.

Los Coronados Islands, of four members small in size, and only some seven miles off the northwestern seacoast, are to be recognized as comprising a differentiation center because of the existence there of a peculiar race of the Song Sparrow (*Melospiza melodia*). This is the only instance in which any of the islands fringing Lower California have been reached or, rather, permanently occupied by this plastic type of bird. Its restricting ecologic requirements doubtless account for this exclusiveness, which is manifest also over the greater part of the peninsular mainland.

A race of Linnet (*Carpodacus mexicanus*) separate from that of the adjacent mainland also occupies Los Coronados Islands. But its affinities are clearly with the Linnets of the Santa Barbara group of islands to the northwestward, off southern Upper California. Another product of what may be termed the S·

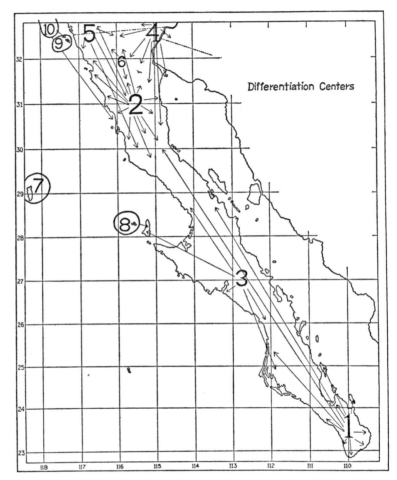

Differentiation centers as having likely influenced the avian history of Lower California: 1, Cape District; 2, San Pedro Mártir District; 3, San Ignacio District; 4, Colorado Desert District; 5, San Diegan District; 6, Sierra Juárez District; 7, Guadalupe Island; 8, San Benito Islands; 9, Los Coronados Islands; 10, Santa Barbara Islands.

Barbara Island differentiation area is the peculiar warbler, *Vermivora celata sordida,* which reaches not only to certain of the coastal islands at the north but to a few known mainland localities close to the seacoast even as far south as 30° latitude. These stations, both insular and mainland, show obvious similarities of environment, both vegetational and climatic, to such an island of the Santa Barbara group as San Clemente.

Curiously, not one of the numerous Lower Californian islands in the Gulf has as yet been shown to possess an avian differentiate, although several of them do possess endemic members of other classes of vertebrates. However, cases of differentiation among the most sedentary types of birds may yet be discovered, when extensive collections of satisfactory material have been studied.

Reviewing the differentiation areas of Lower California, it can be said that the Cape District appears to have acted most potently with respect to bird life, as indicated on both the criterion of numbers of differentiates recognizable and that of great amount of difference characterizing some of them (for example, *Basilinna, Junco, Turdus*). The San Pedro Mártir District comes next on the former criterion, Guadalupe Island on the latter criterion. Important factors in the development of an area as a separate center of avian differentiation are, I should say, as follows: (1) Presence of many and diverse ecologic niches; (2) presence of marked climatic peculiarities as contrasted with the territories whence the species are being derived by the process of pioneering; (3) degree of isolation by barriers of water or of terrain inhospitable to the existence of those species which do find favorable living conditions in the area in question; (4) size of the area in question, or rather, of the portions of it furnishing the different ecologic niches. (A mere dab of a certain niche, as comprised in marshland or forest of but a few acres' extent, does not often suffice to support permanent populations of appropriate species, no matter how well suited to their requirements.)

A differentiation center of strong potency will produce differentiates some at least of which will penetrate far beyond the confines of the immediately effective area. Some of the species are prolific of individuals, aggressive, and adaptable with respect to being able to thrive under quite a range of ecologic conditions. These, in continually radiating streams of individuals, involving successive generations in relatively short series, often extend unmodified along routes of least environmental resistance even quite through adjacent differentiation areas. Especially is this the case where the neighboring areas are of weak potency. The accompanying map of Lower California (fig. 1 [of the original publication]) studied in connection with the detailed statements of distribution in the text under the general accounts of the species, provides numerous illustrations of the principles here stated.

Significance of Faunal Analysis
for General Biology

IS THERE any far-reaching significance, for general biology, in the sort of faunal exploration which results in the describing and listing of species and subspecies and the working out in detail of their ranges? Yes, I would answer with no hesitation whatsoever. For, in dealing with the ranges of animals, more particularly in determining and examining the limits of their habitats, in ascertaining the diagnostic characters of the species and more especially of the subspecies, and in discovering correlations between these characters and various factors of the environment, we are scrutinizing evolution now *in progress*.

Among the numerous races of Upper and Lower Californian birds, for example, we are able to pick out, here and there, practically every appreciable stage in the general differentiation process, from neighboring stocks differing so slightly from one another as to show only faint departures when long series of individuals are averaged, to the fully differentiated species in the true, or Linnaean sense, namely, as set off sharply by itself without there being any individuals that can be interpreted as even hybrids with a neighboring species. Where connectants exist, intergrades we call them in our present system, the races thus *incompletely* differentiated we call subspecies. There is no difference, genetically, between the subspecies and the species, or in any other way save for this one, of more or less casual circumstance, intergradation, and, usually, of the correlated lesser amount of difference between allied subspecies.

Much objection has been registered of late from many lay, and curiously some professional, sources against the recognition of subspecies in nomenclature, on the ground that they are difficult of discernment; and their recognition, it is urged, is therefore of no practical utility. But, I ask, is the histologist, or the embryologist, or the bacteriologist expected to confine his labors within limits easily comprehended by the laity? Why, then, should the faunal zoologist be expected to keep *his* investigations within any such bounds? Personally, as a student of vertebrate speciation I am only mildly interested in the full, Linnaean species, because the full species has passed the really significant stage in its career: I am intensely interested in the barely discernible subspecies, because *it* is in the critical, formative stage, and there is a good chance that I may learn something of the causes and essential conditions of its differentiation.

To my mind, then, in the study of subspecies as contrasted with the so-called full species we are dealing with the earliest stages in the phylogenetic process. In other words, subspecies are the fundamental elements which, in any really significant systematic and faunistic investigation, must receive primary recognition. The more accurately and acutely we can train our senses and instruments upon the detection of subspecies, the better understanding will we gain of their nature and the processes producing them.

Recalling now the maps of Upper and Lower California, and having in mind the ranges of the avian inhabitants of that continuous territory, in so far as knowledge of them has accumulated, we observe some significant things. In many of the groups of wide representation we find that the amount of difference displayed by the geographic forms varies directly with the degree of spatial separation.

For example, take the bird group containing the California Linnet, genus *Carpodacus:* In comparison with the mainland race, the stock on Los Coronados Islands, seven miles offshore, is appreciably but not constantly nor conspicuously different. The linnets of the San Benito Islands, 40 miles from the nearest mainland shore, show somewhat greater amount of, and fairly constant, differences from the birds of the mainland, while the race on Guadalupe Island, 135 miles from the opposite mainland, is most different of all, so widely different and so constantly so, that it is designated as a full species. The features which characterize this Guadalupe species as compared with the mainland linnet are much greater size, especially of bill and skull, longer legs, but relatively shorter wing bones, and shorter keel of sternum (Lucas, 1891). These latter, skeletal differences, as pointed out by Lucas, reflect loss in wing power. This tendency reaches its extreme on certain remote Pacific islands where, in other families of birds, a condition of complete flightlessness is found. Before man's advent the land birds on the islands were without enemies and, their confines being limited, there was little or no need or opportunity for quick or prolonged flights.

Now, going southward from the San Francisco Bay region through California and the northern two-thirds of the mainland peninsula of Lower California, the linnets are (to me) indistinguishably the same all the way. Let it be noted that there are no barriers anywhere in this long extent of territory to prevent free interbreeding of the birds from place to place and progressive intermingling from generation to generation. South of latitude 30°, however, a noticeable change in the characters of the birds becomes apparent, until in the southern half of the peninsula an easily definable mainland subspecies exists, of smaller size and brighter color. In this latter case, where no water barrier interposes itself, the factor of long *distance* has become influential as an effective form of isolation, permitting differentiation of the remote stocks despite commingling over intervening territory. The long *time* involved, in combination with long distance, here compensates for lack of an impassable barrier. Also, there are markedly different climatic areas concerned.

To put the matter perhaps more concisely, separation of descent lines, even though close together spatially, by impassable barriers, brings rapid differentiation, relatively speaking; whereas, *without* the intervention of positive barriers, there is required a long interval of distance or a very long time, most effectively both, for the impress upon two stocks, of subspecific characters.

I will mention just one other, out of the numerous cases which in the aggregate force one to recognize the potency of geographic isolation in the initiation of divergent evolution. The linnets just cited belong as a rule to regions of warm climate; their metropolis is toward the south. The Spotted Towhees, of the genus *Pipilo,* a rather more Boreal group than the linnets, occupy territory from British Columbia to as far south as the tip of the Lower California peninsula, but not continuously; they are interrupted in their distribution. Mainland races, it is true, succeed one another gradually south from British Columbia along the Pacific coast, until the southernmost in the continuous series is found in the San Pedro Mártir district. There the continuity ceases. South of that, evidently because of the unfavorable floral and climatic conditions, there are no Spotted Towhees at all on the Lower California peninsula until the Sierra de La Laguna are reached, in the Cape district; there, in a small mountainous area, exists a race of Spotted Towhee considerably different from the race of the San Pedro Mártir district. The amount of difference is greater than in the case of the *linnet* of the Cape region. *Also,* there is a wide, uninhabited geographic hiatus in the case of the Spotted Towhee, such as does not exist in the case of the linnet.

Only one of the Lower California islands is inhabited by the Spotted Towhee, Guadalupe, 135 miles offshore, whose high and cold summit is most nearly of all of them Boreal or northern in its climatic features. And the form of Spotted Towhee, of Guadalupe Island is even more different from the Upper Californian towhee than is the one in the Cape district.

It is to be observed in these and several paralleling cases that the most nearly similar races in a series are not located within the same differentiation area, nor yet in remote differentiation areas, but in separate and adjacent differentiation areas, this being essentially "Jordan's law," one of the several outstanding laws of animal distribution, of great significance for evolutionary process.

Another generalization with important implications comes

from observations upon subspecific behavior where a number of plastic vertebrate types are found in one differentiation area. I will refer in particular to my ornithological findings in the peculiar climatic area comprised in the San Pedro Mártir section of northern Lower California. Here, between the crest of the Sierra San Pedro Mártir and the Pacific, is what may be termed a *humid desert;* that is to say, there exists a region of meager rainfall but of high atmospheric humidity. Fog or cloudiness is frequent over an intensely dry terrane!

The notable thing is that this combination of conditions brings similar modifications (deepened coloration, certain proportions of wing and tail, lesser size of bill, etc.) in various birds which are very remotely related to one another phylogenetically; for example, in certain flycatchers, finches, and woodpeckers. In other words, subjection of very different stocks to the same peculiar set of critically important conditions has brought parallel modifications in certain functions and structures. The inherited variations have not been random, but have been directed—orthogenetic. Hence, I think, subspecific characters, either intrinsically themselves or as, perhaps sometimes, linked, only, with others that are, must be of *worthy* sorts in the racial struggle for existence—not, ordinarily, indifferent or useless ones.

And so it is by the accumulation of group studies of this sort that the student of faunas finds himself led to interpretations of seemingly great significance in the problem of species formation. The same or similar interpretations, I believe, extend to the origin of the larger groups, as well as to all the ultimate differentiations, up to man himself, and all his races.

We have heard a great deal of late years in regard to evolution through mutation. A long list of papers and books has been written relative to germinal constitution and variations, wherein, if not directly so implied in the title, the reader is induced to believe that the problem of evolution of species is being immediately dealt with. To my mind, this assumption involves a most astonishing illogicality. Of course it goes without saying that change of species through time could not take place without the circumstance of inheritance; but neither could it without such qualities, features, or processes as assimilation, metabolism, hormone production, growth, cell division, reproduction in the large. Each and all of these things and many others are vital to the existence and persistence of living beings; but they may, indeed probably, have nothing directly to do with change of specific type through time.

In regard to all these matters it is important to know, to the farthest detail, the nature of the mechanisms and processes involved. But the set of facts having to do with inheritance is not properly to be confused with, or to be thought of as supplanting, those concerned directly with the origination of species. No matter *how* heritable variations in individuals may arise, no evolution in the phylogenetic sense can have taken place until said variations have been subjected to the drastic process of trial for survival. This endurance test is imposed by environments. And the critical factor for divergence of stocks under differing environments is isolation. Otherwise there is swamping, with resulting uniformity of populations, instead of divergence. Of course, the amount and rapidity of effect by environment is immediately limited by the conservatism of the organism—the animal will stand only so much ecologic pressure. Its inheritance prescribes a certain limit of modifiability; but counting that in—then, with a more or less segregated population, whose variations are of the inherited sort, the Darwinian factor of *selection* comes into play. These heritable variations of selectional value are of small compass, certainly not of large amount, as the old "mutation" concept had it.

By the action of selection a population is able to accommodate itself to conditions as they change; it becomes less liable to outright extinction should conditions change abruptly. Animal adaptation, so-called, is merely the demonstration of a capacity to survive under conditions at the moment existing—just that! And animals do just as little adaptation as they can and "get by." Inertia is a characteristic of the organism. The *direction* of such modifications as *are* acquired is determined by the course of environmental history.

The accumulating experience of the field naturalist is bringing conviction that the incipient species in nature, the subspecies, owes its origin to a process, on a vast scale, of trial, discard, and preservation, of individuals, and of groups of individuals comprising populations, which populations from generation to generation are thereby rendered more nearly adjusted to such environments as they can endure at all. But environments themselves never stabilize; they are changing, proliferating, evolving continually. A balanced state of perfect adaptation of the organism can never be attained, but only continually approached, such approach being forced, under penalty of extinction.

It seems to me, then, that the problem of the origin of species ought to be dissociated largely from the problems of inheritance. The problem of speciation would seem to lie much more nearly to the provinces of the geographer and climatologist than to that of the geneticist. The studies of the systematist, if he be also a field zoologist, in his definition of minor species and of subspecies, and of the geographer, may be looked to, accordingly, if properly correlated, to bring an improved understanding of the conditions, methods, and results of evolution, more especially as regards the higher vertebrate types.

Linnets and Dandelions

IS IT FEASIBLE to blend sentiment with natural history and at the same time maintain fairly high factual and rational standards?

My wife and I live in the fully built-up part of Berkeley that lies toward Oakland, and our house faces east. The house on the lot next north of ours is set far back; and in front of it and overlooked from certain of our north windows is a broad lawn. This lawn, until last year, was our neighbor's pride; but latterly, the aggressive dandelion gained a roothold and very quickly spread throughout the plot. This invasion by dandelions, a seeming calamity to the owner of the lawn, led, however, to pleasurable satisfaction on the part of certain other people in the neighborhood, and even likely, though unconsciously, to the owner himself.

To persons living in the residence district of almost any California town, the bird voice of most cheerfully appealing sound in springtime is that of our linnet or house finch. There are two critical circumstances that apparently determine the local presence or absence of linnets: food in the form of seeds of composite plants, and near-by shelter of a completely enveloping type. The seeding dandelions, in the neighborhod I describe, furnished a preferred food; and the untrimmed vines, with their accumulated débris, on the walls of some of the older houses, furnished the preferred types of roosting and nesting places. These features offering, then, along in March, the linnets dropped into our neighborhood, three pairs of them.

The rough-surfaced, now old-fashioned, wood shingles of the roofs provided singing-posts for the male linnets. Each of the three red-heads now has his separate place near or on a gable end, used each day for his singing and dancing. The daily program of the linnets begins at broad daylight, with intermittent song from the roosts in the vines. Then, shortly, with heightened vigor and, to the human ear, the acme of cheerfulness, each singer, often followed closely by his mate, mounts to the roof and greets the first flood of sunshine. From five to seven, these past mornings, when city sounds have not yet swelled to overwhelming volume, we hear the linnets pour forth their songs—of racing rhythm, of many falling, but always also rising, inflections.

And then, about seven, as the sunshine first sweeps the plot which our north windows overlook, each of the three pairs of linnets goes to foraging on the lawn, seeking out the seedheads of the dandelions. Each female is closely attended by a jealous male; each pair keeps to itself in a different segment of the lawn. We observe them, and we are amused by many a little, humanlike amenity.

The lowly yellow dandelion, it is true, is despised by some people whose first heed is to the severe demands of convention; but may not many of us be justified in looking upon that so-called weed as indirectly but essentially responsible for the early morning chorus of bird voices that greets our receptive ears? For the suburban bird-lover, the day begins with cheerful sound, and maybe the whole day proves brighter for it. Optimism prevails where a degree of gloom might have held sway.

To outline, in review, the picture just drawn: Oldish houses with untrimmed vines about them; rather informal, therefore carefree, householders; lawns with dandelions in them; then linnets; and *therefore,* mornings and evenings, the neighborhood pervaded by the most heartening of California bird songs.

A Revised Life-Zone Map
of California

SOME NATURALISTS, especially in the western United States, find use for the life-zone system of expressing animal and plant distribution. The present writer is one of these. The last attempt, so far as known to him, to outline the life-zones of the entire state of California resulted in the map published in 1913 in connection with his "Distributional List of the Mammals of California" (Grinnell, Proc. Calif. Acad. Sci., ser. 4, 3:265–390, pls. 15, 16). That same map, with no modification, was published subsequently in two other places; the map as issued herewith has been entirely revised. Many parts of California not gone over prior to 1913 have now been visited by me personally; also much new information has become accessible through publication by other field workers, both zoölogists and botanists. Several intensive faunal and floral studies of restricted sections of the State have been reported upon, and pertinent data in these reports have here been used.

The plotting of life-zones in the field in practice is done on the basis of the presence or absence of "indicators." The chief of these, for California, have been catalogued elsewhere (Hall and Grinnell, Proc. Calif. Acad. Sci., ser. 4, 9, 1919:37–67). In that paper, also, the "life-zone concept" is concisely defined, the method of using indicators is described, and "precautions" are advised concerning the measure of dependence to be placed on individual indicators.

While a thoroughgoing review of the life-zone problem cannot be undertaken here, it *is* appropriate to refer to two recent criticisms that have been made of the basic "laws" of temperature control originally formulated by C. Hart Merriam (see Kendeigh, Wilson Bull., 44, 1932:129–143; Shelford, *idem*, 144–157 [each of these articles accompanied by a full bibliography]). In respect to these authoritative criticisms it may be remarked that, although the exact factorial components of gross "temperature" have not yet been worked out satisfactorily, no one with adequate field experience can doubt that objectively determinable zones of life having a general relation to temperature do exist and that the limits of these zones are imposed upon plant and animal occurrences, in part, at least, directly, by variations in climatic temperature beyond certain critical levels. There is, to be sure, varying tolerance to this general factor by different species; but the observed extreme sensitiveness to it of so many kinds of organisms, and especially of such warm-blooded and motile animals as certain humming-birds and bats, is convincing.

The mapping of the zones of California as now offered on a small scale, while far from ideal, is probably about the best that can be done with our present available knowledge of plant and animal distribution. Data for mapping on a larger scale, with more detail, have not been gathered, at least for any extensive part of the State. Perhaps rather fortunately, on a map so small-scaled as the present one, finer indication of local zonation and of zonal "spotting" is not practicable. The boundaries shown are only approximate; intricate local deviations in topographically rough country are not shown. Each line is thus drawn as an average for the position of a boundary between two zones, ignoring too fine interdigitations as well as small detached areas, even where more accurately known; in very many places I have no adequate records of them. Sometimes a detached bit of a given zone surrounded by a great extent of a higher or a lower zone will be represented larger—must be, to show at all—than it really is.

Because, further, of the necessities imposed by small-scale mapping, the three divisions of the Boreal life-zone, namely, Alpine-Arctic, Hudsonian, and Canadian, are colored together, with the tone, green, which conventionally designates Canadian. This is not so very inappropriate, however, since, of the three divisions, Canadian, in California, is much the most extensive.

It should be kept in mind that the term "boundary" is used here as meaning approximately the middle of the belt of mergence between two zones. There is rarely any really sharp demarcation in faunal or floral character where two zones adjoin. Furthermore, as already implied, it is frankly to be stated that in parts of the State, notably in places along the western flank of the Sierra Nevada, the positions of boundaries have been plotted inferentially. Where the ground has not been actually traversed, or has not been examined directly from more or less distance, then contours of elevation from United States Geological Survey topographic sheets have been relied upon together with correlated knowledge.

A circumstance of decided help in field plotting of life-zones, and one doubtless of some significance, came to my attention in May and June of 1933, east of the fog belt in Trinity and Humboldt counties. I observed that, on the slopes of South Fork Mountain, the lower limit of the previous winter's accumulation of snow still remaining on the ground to any depth coincided closely with the lower limit of the Canadian life-zone. This checked with my own knowledge of the indicators there, obtained in the summers of preceding years; and on the basis of this coincidence I felt justified in plotting from a distance the Canadian life-zone on peaks and ridges which I had not been over. The area of snow remaining so long after the close of winter seemed to accord with certain factors which modified the effects of altitude alone. Some of these were cardinal direction of slope, air flow, and mountain shadows. The deferred summer-time activities of animals as well as plants above the "snow line" at this season were certainly suggestive of high-zone conditions. However, this criterion for life-zone plotting could not be used within the humid coast belt; and it would have to be checked closely with ascertained biotic conditions to be useful in any other kind of climatic area.

I must, from my personal experience, warn those who use the life-zone system against a kind of error likely to be committed in field work. When a person has lived, or has been working for long, in one zone, and then enters an adjacent zone, the first met-with indicators (individual plants or animals) of the adjacent zone inevitably impress him, and unduly so. He will, as a result, plot the margin of that zone nearer to the zone of his acquaintance than the mean line of mergence between the two zones. Of course later, with better balanced basis of judgment, the worker may make the needed shift in the plotted position of the boundary. Eventually, statistical, quantitative handling of indicators on extensive areas will probably be possible and will serve for determining with great precision just where zonal limits lie.

Up-hill Planters

THE SECOND WEEK of October, a year ago, found me nature-watching on the western slope of the southern Sierra Nevada. I was walking along the road which leads up to Sequoia National Park, when, as the morning sunshine began to increase the warmth and dryness of the atmosphere, I began to note the sounds of falling and bouncing acorns. For, at the level where I was, about 5000 feet, the black oaks were just then yielding their annual crop of seeds. It would seem that these seeds are finally loosened from their cups, if not disturbed otherwise, when the air each day has reached a certain measure of dryness.

The mountain slope was steep, 25 to 45 degrees; and along about ten to eleven o'clock the sound and sight of descending acorns was impressive. They were even accumulating in appreciable windrows in places along the inside of the road next to the bank; now and then one, from source far up-slope, having gained extra momentum, bounced clear over the road and proceeded on its way toward the canyon bottom far below.

Acorns are smooth-shelled, heavy objects, and those of the black oak in particular, are of rotund shape. These qualities make for insecurity of placement on any slope upon which they fall, until in their movements they reach some arresting crevice, or some sufficiently wide strip of level, or nearly level, ground on which to find lodgment.

It was clear to me that the direction of seed scattering from any one oak tree was here well-nigh directly down-hill. In that place and on that day I saw *no* acorn moving *up*-hill. Gravity alone was acting as the agency of distribution. There appeared no possibility that *wind* could serve as an agent of elevation, as with seeds of such trees as maple, cottonwood and willow. In the case of the oaks, it might therefore seem, the only possible direction of general forest spreading through time would have to be through the action of gravity and streams of water, always down-hill. But how, then, could forests ever have spread, naturally, so as to gain altitude on our many mountain sides?

The next two days, October 12 and 13, my companion, Dr. Eric Hill, and I spent seeking pocket-gophers down near Three Rivers, about 1000 feet altitude, in the valley of the lower Kaweah River. Here another kind of oak, the blue oak, abounded, and we observed that there was a fairly good crop of its acorns, though not borne as uniformly as those of the black oak in the life-zone above. Very many of the blue oaks had produced no acorns that season. Especially was this true of the trees far up the hillsides above the valley bottom. Some of the trees had produced a few acorns. Those trees which were bearing most heavily were those of larger, thriftier-looking condition, down toward the river bottom. Of certain possible bearing on our problem, this season was a dry one; and furthermore it was the latest of a series of dry years.

As we tended our trap-lines, run in all the different types of soil within reach, we became aware of the presence and especially the activities of California Jays (*Aphelocoma californica*). These activities looked into, became of deep significance to us; for here, indeed, was the agency at this particular place, at this particular time, of transportation of acorns up-hill. The jays we saw to be centering their interest in those most abundantly fruiting trees down in the bottom of the canyon. There the birds were gathering the acorns and carrying them up the slopes, to be ensconced in various hidey-holes, some of them to be buried, after the well-known blue-jay tradition, in the ground of open spaces on the hillsides. From morning to evening, individual birds were almost constantly in sight when we looked out of the auto cabin where we worked, 150 yards from the river.

Every bird going up-slope bore an acorn lengthwise in its bill; every bird in return course was empty-billed. If I had only thought of it, here was a chance for counting birds, and their loads, in sight, during, say, a three-hour period; and then computing the bushels of blue-oak acorns being elevated by the jays perhaps hundreds of feet each October day in that one valley.

In this same locality of observation, Dr. Hill and I saw "digger" ground squirrels busily gathering acorns that had fallen to the ground, carrying them in various directions (with these animals, however, irrespective of direction of slope) to their burrows or to their shelling stations. Twice we watched a ground squirrel climb up a blue oak to the larder of a group of California Woodpeckers, filling its cheek pouches with the acorns they had gathered and stored, even though being attacked by the resentful birds. Then the squirrel would go precipitately down the trunk and off to its own cache in the ground.

Observations of the type just cited, gathered into notebook and memory from many parts of California, have led me to generalize concerning the paramount agency of vertebrate animals in the dispersal of trees, especially of oaks. My recollections bring into this credit column, not only California Jays, woodpeckers, and ground squirrels, but also gray squirrels, chickarees, chipmunks and wood rats, and Steller Jays and Band-tailed Pigeons. In reflecting upon this matter, we can see readily that the relationship is of reciprocal benefit; all of these animal agents of seed dispersal are supplied, at least in part, by the oaks with food, or shelter, and (or) nursery sites. The trees produce crops of nutritious seeds—each seed nutritious either to the prospective oaklet or to the animal that eats it—in vast excess of immediate seeding needs. There is enormous seeming extravagance on the part of the trees, far and away greater production than would be needed to provide for persistence of the species, *if* the species were of fixed geographic position through time. Granting an individual longevity of 75 to 300 years for more or less mature oaks of one kind and another (I cite Jepson, The Silva of California, 1910, p. 57), perhaps one successful germination to only a million acorns would provide for mere forest replacement. Even this ratio is probably far too high. The point I wish to make is that in the long-time interests of the tree species, involving locomotion of the whole *forest*, there is value received upon this huge rate of production. It is not extravagance, but good investment, for the oaks to provide subsistence for a continuing population of animal associates.

Even in any relatively brief period of years, catastrophe may overtake the fortunes of the oak forest. Fire of great intensity may destroy all of the growths on a given slope clear to the top of the ridge. Then quick recovery—early repopulation by the oaks—will likely be dependent upon the survival and germination of acorns buried previously by animals, in open places, where the heat was least effective, as also upon the year-by-year marginal replanting process just described. I think especially of California's great erosion-guarding and water-conserving chaparral belt, of which the live oaks and scrub oaks of several kinds are prominent constituents—and their constant animal attendants, the California Jays, the chipmunks, and the dusky-footed wood rats.

Giving again to our scientific imagination fair rein, let us think of the oak belts of California in longest time vista—back through not only centuries, but millenniums. Also let us think of the, to us invisible, climatic boundaries which at any one time-level hem in those belts, each belt characterized by a different species of oak. And let us further think how these boundaries have shifted in past time spatially, as borne upon by changes in physical conditions affecting climate—those involved in repeated elevation and depression of the land surface, and in shiftings of prevailing air currents. We can then think of the oak belts, as slowly marching, through time, up hill and down dale, southward and northward, as their species have been driven by the gradually shifting exigencies of physical requirement which determine where new trees can not only sprout, but mature. Again, we must think, not of the individual tree up to 300 years old, but of the aggregate of trees involving long series of generations of their kind. Such time-space aggregation has been *forced* to move from place to place. It has literally *had* to keep up with the procession. It has *had* to provide ways and means of insuring transportation, or else be wiped out through complete failure at any one level, of those favoring factors which have to do with the existence of each kind of oak in its own life-zone. Tree species have had to move their location from one period to the next or die in a struggle against oncoming adverse conditions.

Here, then, is where a certain portion of the associated animal life has come into the service of the oak species. In the present era, with life-zones probably advancing northward, and up-slope, we can think of the successive belts of valley oaks, blue oaks, golden oaks, black oaks, and huckleberry oaks, on our western mountain-sides, as relying, most especially for that part of their dispersal comprised in elevation, entirely upon their bird and mammal associates. And there obtains that vital exchange of benefits to which I alluded. Plant-animal communities, eventually closely knit in their specific interrelationships, have been subject to evolutionary processes quite as definitely as discrete species.